THE CLASSICAL ATOM

ORIGINS OF QUANTUM PHYSICS
VOLUME I: THE CLASSICAL ATOM

This book is in the
ADDISON-WESLEY SERIES IN PHYSICS

DAVID LAZARUS, *Consulting Editor*

ORIGINS OF QUANTUM PHYSICS

THE CLASSICAL ATOM

by

FRANCIS L. FRIEDMAN

and

LEO SARTORI

Massachusetts Institute of Technology

ADDISON-WESLEY PUBLISHING COMPANY, INC.

READING, MASSACHUSETTS · PALO ALTO · LONDON

NEW YORK · DALLAS · ATLANTA

FOREWORD

In 1955–56 Francis Friedman took a sabbatical leave from the Massachusetts Institute of Technology to work with Niels Bohr in Copenhagen and to write a book, of which this volume is the first part. It was to come out either as a full-length textbook or as a companion piece to an already existing textbook on atomic physics. He felt strongly that insight into the fundamental physics of atomic nature could be fostered by driving the old (Bohr-Sommerfeld) quantum theory further than had been fashionable since the great successes of modern quantum theory. He wanted to exploit the relationship between experiment and interpretation through arguments like that of Bohr's Correspondence Principle. Emphatically, he did not want to proliferate or purvey the mathematical gymnastics of the early twenties. Rather he believed that the simplification of mathematical analysis to its barest essentials could help reveal the essential physics of a problem, and that the simple routes are the clearest and therefore the best pedagogic routes. No one, of course, argues with this idea; but few men with a clarity of mind and an understanding of both experiment and theory possess a talent for exposition to others less learned than themselves. I was one of many of Francis Friedman's colleagues who, like his students, came to him for the point of insight that always makes the difference in the line of argument.

Naturally he had several motives in wanting to write a textbook in atomic physics. He was convinced that texts rarely include the most important and living parts of the arguments. In going from experimental findings to theory, and back around the loop to new experiment and new theory, there are many misleading clues and attractive blind alleys. For many text writers, and for many students, the creative processes of science are hidden. Perhaps Charles Dickens was saying this in the opening lines of *Hard Times:*

" 'Now, what I want is, Facts. Teach these boys and girls nothing but Facts. Facts alone are wanted in life. Plant nothing else, and root out everything else. You can only form the minds of reasoning animals upon Facts: nothing else will ever be of any service to them. This is the principle on which I bring up my own children, and this is the principle on which I bring up these children. Stick to Facts, sir!' . . .

"The speaker and the schoolmaster, and the third grown person present, all backed a little, and swept with their eyes the inclined plane of little vessels then and there arranged in order, ready to have imperial gallons of facts poured into them until they were full to the brim."

The wonderful mixture of vagueness and clarity, the soft ideas and the moments of hard lucidity, the really tight logic and the bits of "it stands to reason" are all part of the game. Original papers frequently contain the substance and the arguments based on the facts available at the time that they appeared. The good student will go to original papers, because the masters knew the pitfalls and the alternatives and sometimes they put them in print. But sometimes they did not, and frequently we need these full arguments in modern dress to make them intelligible and relevant to the student who is desperately trying to leap-frog over the past. Francis Friedman was a master in the art of bringing twentieth century sophistication to the arguments of the nineteenth century. He could do it because he loved both. He loved physics in the making, and he knew that the way to learn how to make physics was to see how it was made. No, it is not just Mr. Dickens' facts, facts, facts, nor the absence of nuances. It is that one of the best ways to learn how to bring understanding out of enigma is to see great minds at work, to see how they succeeded in building out of unbelievably fragmentary clues.

One asks, why the long delay from 1956 to now. The answer is that in 1957 Francis Friedman responded as a whole man (and I sometimes thought he was an army of men) to a call to help the schools. To do this, he laid his manuscript aside, and death came before he could return to it. In his new role he became responsible for the content and intellectual style of the P.S.S.C. physics course. Like this small volume, it shows his stubborn insistence on the first-rate.

It is a pleasure to acknowledge the great service performed by Dr. Leo Sartori, who had been asked to take the manuscript in its unfinished state and complete the writing of the book. This has been done so fully in the spirit of Francis Friedman that it is difficult now for me to see where Friedman leaves off and Sartori begins.

Cambridge, Mass.   Jerrold R. Zacharias

PREFACE

This series of monographs traces the development of atomic physics from its classical foundations through the "old" quantum theory to the birth of modern quantum mechanics. It was in that era of exciting discovery and frustrating quandary that most of the fundamental atomic phenomena first came under close scrutiny. Many explanations proposed during the period are still considered essentially valid and form an important part of today's physics; even wrong theories often turned out to contain the germs of successful later ones. Incorrect models, bold extrapolations, and even some fortunate coincidences played a part in the struggle to make sense out of often perplexing data—a struggle which led finally to the quantum theory. These volumes investigate some blind alleys and fret over puzzling paradoxes before presenting the resolutions, in the belief that increased understanding is thereby attained. They are not primarily a text, but are intended for use as supplementary reading in a course, or for perusal by an interested reader.

Each volume is fairly self-contained, although the first two, which deal with classical physics, in some respects form a logical unit. The first concentrates on the identification of subatomic particles and on atomic models culminating in the nuclear atom; the second treats the electromagnetic properties of matter and the various aspects of the "radiation dilemma." The solution of the dilemma in terms of quantum ideas forms the subject of subsequent volumes.

How this book was begun is related by Dr. Zacharias in the foreword. Shortly after Francis Friedman's untimely death I took on the task of completing his unfinished manuscript, which consisted of mimeographed notes for a course he had taught several times at M.I.T. There were drafts of several chapters and a list of additional subjects to be included. Because of the pressure of Friedman's other endeavors, the manuscript had not been touched in several years.

Friedman's approach was interesting and original. Topics which receive scant mention in most books were carefully analyzed, and much of the discussion was addressed to a mature reader. I have tried to fulfill the potentialities of such an approach, by elaborating on the discussion and extending it to additional topics which, I feel, merit similar attention. In the present volume, Chapter 3 is largely new; less extensive revisions have been made in the other two chapters. In the interest of a more uniform presentation the textbook aspects of the original course notes have been de-emphasized; the treatment of some standard material which is found in most textbooks has been curtailed, and the style has been altered somewhat. It then seemed appropriate to publish the work as a series of short monographs rather than a single lengthy volume.

My involvement in this project was brought about by J. R. Zacharias, D. H. Frisch, and B. T. Feld, to whom I express my appreciation. It is a pleasure to thank A. P. French for much valuable criticism and encouragement, and P. Morrison, J. Tessman, and H. C. White for profitable discussions. The financial support of the Science Teaching Center has enabled me to devote to the book the substantial amount of time it required.

There are undoubtedly many people whom Francis Friedman would have wished to thank. Foremost among them must be Niels Bohr, under whose inspiration the book had its inception. The others, I regret, have to remain unacknowledged.

Cambridge, Massachusetts   L. S.
December 1964

CONTENTS

CHAPTER 1

THE BEGINNINGS OF THE ATOMIC THEORY

1. The laws of combining proportions. Despite its speculative origins which go back to the Greeks, the atomic theory had its real birth in the chemistry of Dalton and his followers in the early nineteenth century. (Dalton's *New System of Chemical Philosophy* was published in 1808.) Two chemical laws were fundamental in the introduction of the idea of atoms: the laws of definite and of multiple proportions. In any given chemical compound, the masses of the elements always appear in a definite proportion. Whenever two elements form more than one compound, the ratios of the definite proportions for the individual compounds are always simple rational fractions. For example, in water the mass of oxygen is always 7.9 times that of hydrogen, whereas in hydrogen peroxide the ratio of oxygen mass to hydrogen mass is 15.8. Thus,

$$\frac{(m_O/m_H)_{\text{peroxide}}}{(m_O/m_H)_{\text{water}}} = 2.$$

The nitrogen-oxygen compounds furnish an even more striking illustration: the combining proportions are $(m_O/m_N) = 0.57, 1.13, 1.71, 2.29,$ and 2.86 for nitrous oxide, nitric oxide, nitrous anhydride, nitrogen dioxide, and nitric anhydride respectively. These numbers are in the ratio of $1:2:3:4:5$.

If elements could be divided into portions of arbitrary size, one would expect that all gradations of chemical composition should exist. The laws of chemical proportions, and especially the appearance of integers in these laws, therefore strongly suggested the existence of some fundamental units in which elements exist or combine. These units were Dalton's atoms.

2. Avogadro's hypothesis. Integers appeared also in another simple law of gas chemistry, Gay-Lussac's law of combining volumes. At any given temperature and pressure, the volumes of two gases which combine completely to form a new compound are related by a simple rational fraction. If the new compound is again gaseous, its volume is also related to those of the others by simple rational fractions: one volume of oxygen and two of hydrogen form two volumes of water vapor.

The law of combining volumes lent further support to the atomic hypothesis. It also led Avogadro to his fundamental conclusion concerning the properties of gases, enunciated in 1811: at the same temperature and pressure, a given volume of any (dilute) gas contains the same number of

1

molecules. (The distinction between atoms and molecules was not clearly realized at first. Dalton had in fact earlier considered the possibility of Avogadro's hypothesis but had rejected it because of confusion between the two concepts.)

Avogadro's hypothesis implies that the relative masses of molecules can be determined without ever having to observe an individual atom or molecule. It is sufficient to measure the relative masses of macroscopic samples of gases under standard conditions. By forming and analyzing compounds, it is possible to extend this method to nongaseous substances and thus construct a complete table of relative atomic masses.* Similarly, with the help of Avogadro's hypothesis a study of the condensation of gases can lead to estimates of the relative dimensions of atoms. The additional assumption required in such an estimate is that solids and liquids are tightly packed, so that their volume is essentially the total volume of all the atoms they contain.

In order to convert the information on relative masses and sizes into absolute terms, it is necessary to count the number of atoms (or molecules) in a macroscopic sample. When the sample is one mole, the number of atoms is N_0, Avogadro's number. The best modern value for N_0 is 6.0225×10^{23}; this number plays a central role in atomic physics because it sets the scale of all atomic quantities. For example, a mole of water, with a mass of 18 gm, has a volume of 18 cm^3. The mass of a water molecule is, therefore, about 3×10^{-23} gm, its volume about 3×10^{-23} cm^3, and its characteristic "radius" about 2 A (2×10^{-8} cm). These are the orders of magnitude of all atomic masses and dimensions. There are several other methods by which the molecular dimensions may be estimated. Since molecules are not rigid spheres, the radius is not a well-defined parameter and the exact values obtained depend on the experiment used to define the size. However, all the size determinations are in qualitative agreement with one another. (See the data in Table 2-5, p. 46.)

There is a second reason for the historical importance of Avogadro's number. The fact that several independent methods of determining N_0 all gave essentially the same value furnished strong support for Avogadro's hypothesis and thus for the existence of atoms. This agreement convinced many skeptical scientists of the validity of the atomic hypothesis. It should be borne in mind, however, that more direct demonstrations of

----

* It would seem reasonable to define a scale of mass so that hydrogen, the lightest atom, has unit mass; Dalton did in fact use such a scale. However, because oxygen combines with so many more elements than does hydrogen, its mass was soon adopted as the standard. More recently the scale was again modified, with carbon as the new standard (see Section 3–4).

the atomicity of matter have subsequently been obtained. Such demonstrations began with the experiments of the 1890's which introduced mass spectroscopy, with the counters of Rutherford and Geiger (1908, 1913) and with x-ray diffraction (1913). These experiments will be discussed later. Here we shall review briefly some of the methods by which N_0 has been determined, not only because of their historical but also because of their intrinsic interest [1].*

3. Electrochemistry and Stoney's electron. One of the most important and exact methods of determining Avogadro's number depends on Faraday's law of electrochemistry, formulated in 1833. When an electric current is passed through a solution, the mass of any substance liberated from the solution is proportional to the total charge which has flowed and to the atomic or molecular weight of the substance. If M_A denotes the liberated mass, A the molecular weight of the substance, and Q_A the electric charge, then

$$M_A = \frac{A Q_A}{n_A F}, \tag{1-1}$$

where $F = 96,520$ coul and n_A is a small integer. The constant F (Faraday's constant) is independent of the nature of the solution, the substance liberated, and the length of time the current flowed.

The ratio m_A/M_A is the number of moles which come out of solution, or $1/N_0$ times the number of molecules. Faraday's law thus implies that the average charge carried per molecule is $n_A e$, where $e = F/N_0$. Since both F and N_0 are universal constants, e is one also.

The integral values of n_A point out the significance of e as the basic unit of electricity. (The value of n_A is, of course, the chemical valence of the ion involved in the electrolysis.) This basic unit was probably recognized by Faraday†; however, he did not commit himself to the atomic picture of electricity (nor did Maxwell, for that matter). The atom of electricity was insisted upon by Stoney, who gave it the name "electron" in 1891. We shall call it the electronic charge or Stoney electron, so as to avoid confusion with the specific particle to which the name electron is now applied. Using the values for N_0 and F already quoted, one obtains for e the value 4.806×10^{-10} esu (1.602×10^{-19} coul). On the other hand, if F and e are known, the relation $F = N_0 e$ furnishes an important method for determining N_0.

---

* S. E. Virgo [1] lists more than eighty experimental determinations of Avogadro's number. (Numbers enclosed in brackets refer to the references listed at the end of each chapter.)

† See also H. Helmholtz [2].

Before describing the measurement of e, we make a couple of remarks stemming from Faraday's law, written in the form

$$\left(\frac{Q}{M}\right)_A = \frac{n_A F}{A}. \tag{1-1a}$$

The quantity $(Q/M)_A$ is the specific charge of the substance A; it is characteristic of the liberated substance A and independent of everything else.   (The inverse $(M/Q)_A$ is called the electrochemical equivalent. Although found in much of the literature, it will not be used here.) Through Eq. (1-1a) the specific charges can be used to determine molecular weights; this type of measurement was an important adjunct to the gas chemistry methods sketched in Section 2.

If all atoms of an element are identical, the specific charge is a property of the individual atom or molecule in solution,

$$\left(\frac{Q}{M}\right)_A = \frac{n_A e}{m_A} = \left(\frac{q}{m}\right)_A$$

where $m_A = A/N_0$ is the mass of a single molecule.   It is tempting to conclude that each ion in solution carries the charge $q_A = n_A e$.   Even though this is indeed true, a purely macroscopic measurement cannot exclude the possibility that n_A may be merely an average value.   This question requires further consideration; it will recur in Section 6 and again in later chapters.

4. The Millikan oil drop experiment.   To complete the determination of N_0 from the relation $F = N_0 e$, we shall briefly describe the measurement of e perfected by Millikan in 1910.   Historically, this experiment is out of order here.   Millikan's work followed, and was motivated by, Thomson's experiments on electrons, to be described in Chapter 3.   In discussing the experiment, we omit all mention of its many difficulties and subtleties; these have been described by Millikan himself [3].

If a small charged body is placed between horizontal condenser plates, the electric field **E** in the condenser may be adjusted to give an upward force which balances the downward pull of gravity on the body.   The body remains at rest if

$$qE = Mg, \tag{1-2}$$

where q and M are the charge and mass of the body.

If the forces are not balanced the body accelerates, but in a viscous medium (such as air) it rapidly attains a constant terminal velocity.   For spheres of radius a moving with velocity v in a medium of viscosity η, the viscous force is given by Stokes' law, $F = 6\pi\eta a v$.   The condition for equilibrium is then

$$qE = Mg + 6\pi\eta av, \tag{1-3}$$

where v is the terminal velocity, assumed to be upward.

If the density is known, the viscous drag on a spherical body may be used to determine its radius and mass. When the electric field is turned off, the sphere falls with the terminal velocity, $+v_f$, determined by

$$Mg + 6\pi\eta a(-v_f) = 0. \tag{1-4}$$

Since $M = \frac{4}{3}\pi a^3 \rho$, where ρ is the density, Eq. (1-4) gives

$$a = \left(\frac{9\eta v_f}{2\rho g}\right)^{1/2}. \tag{1-5}$$

Consequently Eq. (1-3) can be rewritten as

$$q = \alpha(v + v_f), \tag{1-6}$$

with

$$\alpha = \frac{18\pi\eta^{3/2}}{E}\left(\frac{v_f}{2\rho g}\right)^{1/2}.$$

All the quantities which appear in the last equation may be determined experimentally; the charge on the body is thus found by measuring its rate of rise in the condenser and its rate of fall when the field is absent.

In Millikan's experiment, oil drops were sprayed into a condenser and observed with a microscope. Oil drops were employed to avoid the excessive evaporation experienced with water, that is, to maintain the spheres at constant radius and mass. As the spheres were slightly too small for Stokes' law to hold exactly, small corrections were determined empirically.

The velocity of the oil drops in field-free fall, as well as their velocity of rise when carrying a moderate charge, could be measured. By turning the electric field on and off Millikan was able, occasionally, to keep one oil drop in the field of view of the microscope for a considerable period of time. Sometimes a change in the charge on a drop was observed; such changes could be induced by ionization of the surrounding air, produced for example with x-rays or with cathode or β-rays.

The existence of a basic electronic charge was clearly indicated by the experiments in which a single oil drop was followed while it picked up and lost charges several times. The differences between any two velocities of rise were always of the form

$$v_i - v_j = nv_0, \tag{1-7}$$

with v_0 a velocity characteristic of the particular experiment, and n a small integer, sometimes unity. The differences between the charges carried could then be expressed as

$$q_i - q_j = n(\alpha v_0). \tag{1–8}$$

This result confirmed the atomicity of electric charge, and the best value obtained for αv_0 could be identified with the Stoney electron. From his original experiment, Millikan found $e = 4.774 \times 10^{-10}$ esu.* Later, because of a discrepancy with other determinations of e, the viscosity of air was carefully remeasured and a slight error in the accepted value was found; this changed the values of the α's by about $\frac{1}{2}\%$, and Millikan's result became $e = 4.8036 \times 10^{-10}$ esu. The value of Avogadro's number obtained from this result is in excellent agreement with other accurate determinations.

5. **Perrin's mass determination of N_0.** Every relation which involves Avogadro's number furnishes a way of measuring it. If the size of an individual molecule can be determined, then a value for N_0 is obtained from the relation $V_A = N_0 v_A$, where V_A is the volume of a mole and v_A that of a molecule. Similarly, if the mass of a molecule, m_A, can be measured, then N_0 follows from the defining relation $M_A = N_0 m_A$.

Various methods have been used to determine the atomic or molecular volume. The most accurate, the determination of interatomic spacing by x-ray diffraction experiments in crystals, is described in Volume II of this series. This method competes favorably with the determination based on measurement of e. Like the latter, it is historically relatively recent (1912). Cruder estimates of molecular volumes provided some of the first values of Avogadro's number; the very first, that of Loschmidt in 1865, falls in this class. These early estimates were based on the kinetic theory of gases, which is treated in the next chapter.

Here we turn to the determination based on a mass measurement. At the outset it must be stated that, in a certain sense, such a determination has never been performed directly. The difficulty in measuring the mass of a single molecule is, briefly, that the molecule is too small. However, an ingenious resolution of this difficulty was devised by Perrin, who succeeded in constructing artificial "pseudomolecules": objects large enough to be measured directly and yet small enough to behave like molecules. With the aid of the pseudomolecules, Perrin obtained a mass determination of Avogadro's number. His argument was based on the density distribution in an isothermal atmosphere (law of atmospheres).

---

* It should be emphasized that Millikan measured the electronic charge e, *not* the charge of the electron. The two are equal, but the equality was not directly established until later. (See end of Section 3–3.)

Consider a gas in the earth's gravitational field, at uniform temperature T. To move a volume V through a pressure differential dp requires the work $V\,dp$. If the gas is in equilibrium, this work is supplied at the expense of a loss in gravitational potential energy, $Mg\,dz$, where M is the mass of the volume V. The condition for equilibrium is, therefore,

$$Mg\,dz + V\,dp = 0. \qquad (1\text{--}9)$$

If we use the ideal gas law,

$$pv = nRT, \qquad (1\text{--}10)$$

where n is the number of moles in the volume V, then (1–9) becomes

$$\frac{M}{n}\,g\,dz + RT\,\frac{dp}{p} = 0. \qquad (1\text{--}11)$$

The quantity M/n is the molecular weight M_A of the gas which makes up the atmosphere. The solution of (1–11) is, therefore,

$$p = p_0 e^{-M_A g(z-z_0)/RT}. \qquad (1\text{--}12)$$

Equation (1–12) shows that a measurement of the temperature and the density distribution in a gaseous atmosphere determines the molecular weight M_A. Before this result can be used to find N_0 it is necessary to know also m_A, the mass of one molecule, which is difficult to measure for ordinary gases. On the other hand, macroscopic particles, whose mass is easily measured, do not ordinarily behave like an ideal gas. However, it was already known at the time of Perrin's experiments that small particles could be suspended in a fluid of comparable density and that they moved about at random (Brownian motion) as the molecules of a gas were supposed to move according to kinetic theory. Such phenomena had been studied since 1827. It was also known that, at least for some purposes, large molecules in solutions behave as a perfect gas. This type of evidence is summarized by the laws of Raoult and Van't Hoff [4]. Perrin, therefore, had reason to hope that he could create an isothermal atmosphere made of particles large enough to measure.

Perrin prepared an emulsion of nearly uniform particles from gamboge, a dried vegetable latex; he determined the density of the particles by equilibration in a solution and their size by measuring their free fall in a viscous medium. The mass of the individual artificial molecules was thus established. By carefully counting the particles in the field of a high-powered microscope, Perrin was able to measure the relative density of the gamboge molecules at various heights in a suspension. After a correction was made for the buoyant force of the fluid, the distribution was in agreement with Eq. (1–12), and the effective molecular weight of the gamboge particles could be determined. Perrin's interesting experiments are described in detail in his own book [4]. In his best determination he used particles of radius 0.367μ, and counted a total of 17,000 particles at various elevations. The value obtained for Avogadro's number, 6.8×10^{23}, was a quite accurate result considering the nature of the experiment. As a result of Perrin's work, the atomic mass units were placed on an absolute mass scale.

6. **Other measurements of N_0; the identity of atoms.** Historically, the first accurate determination of Avogadro's number was a by-product of the researches of Planck on blackbody radiation. Planck was looking for an accurate description of the frequency spectrum and the energy density of electromagnetic radiation in thermal equilibrium. Such an accurate description cannot be obtained from classical physics; the quantum of action was indeed introduced by Planck in order to explain the shape of the blackbody spectrum as measured by Lummer and Pringsheim. Avogadro's number can be determined from Planck's constant h and Boltzmann's constant k, by an argument which will be described in Volume II. The value which Planck obtained in 1900 is in excellent agreement with modern determinations. It is better than most subsequent measurements of N_0, such as, for example, those of Perrin described above.

Determinations of Avogadro's number have also been made in a more direct manner. Although these measurements are generally not so precise as the ones already mentioned, they are very straightforward and lend further strong support to the atomic hypothesis. They are based on the possibility of counting individual events, of adding up individual particles one by one. In principle, what one would like to do in such an experiment is to take a mole of a substance and disassociate it into individual molecules. If these molecules could be forced through some device which records a count each time a molecule passes, the exact number of molecules in a mole would be counted directly. Precautions would have to be taken to ensure that the device really responded every time a molecule passed and never counted a molecule twice. One would also have to be sure that each molecule was thoroughly disassociated from its neighbors, so that molecules did not pass as clusters and falsify the count. Such assurances would already require a great deal of knowledge about the properties of molecules, and an ideal experiment of this type is by no means easy to perform. However, the invention of charged-particle counters, to be described in Chapter 3, made it possible to realize the basic plan. With these counters Rutherford and Geiger determined the number of α-particles emitted per second by a gram of radium. Measurement of the total volume of helium produced by radium in a specified time interval then yielded a determination of Avogadro's number. Such measurements were carried out by Dewar (1908) and by Boltwood and Rutherford (1911). The method was fairly inaccurate, largely because of the difficulty in measuring minute amounts of helium (163 mm^3 per year per gram of radium). Nevertheless the results for N_0 were correct within 10%.

A variant of this method was based on measurement of the lifetime of radium, together with the number of α-particles emitted per second per gram, ν. Since the decay rate decreases as $e^{-t/\tau}$, the total number of α-particles emitted by a mole of radium is

$$N = M \int_0^\infty \nu e^{-t/\tau}\, dt = M\nu\tau,$$

where M is the atomic weight of radium. If it is assumed that every radium atom decays, it follows that N is Avogadro's number. The errors in determinations based on such measurements were also fairly large.

The measurement of the α-particle charge by Rutherford and Geiger See Section 3-7) was also used, in conjunction with Faraday's constant, to determine N_0 in the manner already discussed. This was, in fact, the most accurate of the determinations based on counter data.

Although atomicity was demonstrated in a direct way by the counter experiments, it should be emphasized that the charge and mass of each carrier were still determined only as average values. Many particles had to pass through the counter before a total charge was accumulated sufficient to be accurately measured. The experiments therefore did not measure individual charges, even though they counted individual particles. It is characteristic of all experiments, even including the modern ones, that when they involve natural molecules instead of artificially created ones, they always refer to the properties of a large collection of those molecules. Consequently, although a quite precise and unique value for Avogadro's number can be obtained, it is not possible to establish without doubt that the charge is always the same or that the masses of all the molecules are identical. Average values automatically result as a consequence of performing macroscopic experiments.

Actually, the Millikan experiment (which as already noted is historically out of order here) demonstrated that charges come in units of the Stoney electron e. With this knowledge one can confidently reject the possibility that the counting experiments measure an average over a continuous charge distribution among the carriers. However, the evidence thus far presented does not demand a unique mass for each atom of a chemical substance. Likewise, no convincing evidence has as yet been brought forth for equality in size or shape among the atoms of each chemical species.

In summary, then, the acceptance of an atomic hypothesis, the establishment of Avogadro's number, and even the recognition of a basic unit of charge do not necessarily imply that every atom of a given chemical species is identical with all the others. Nevertheless, this was generally supposed to be the case by research workers in the nineteenth century, beginning with Dalton. It is interesting to consider what other evidence can be brought to bear on the question of identity or nonidentity of the individual atoms.

Before Avogadro's number had been determined, it was to some extent easier to argue that all atoms of the same chemical element are identical. The reason is that the number is so unimaginably large. Before this fact was known, an argument could be made from the identical properties of macroscopic samples of matter. If, for example, all water molecules were not identical, one might expect to observe occasional variations in the properties of 1-cc samples of water. Most samples would contain an average number of molecules of each type, determined by their relative abundance. Once in a while, however, a sample should, by chance, contain an excess of molecules of one particular type; the properties of such a sample would differ in some way from the average. The high precision with which macroscopic samples of the same chemical substance are reproducible is, apparently, an argument against any variation in the individual building blocks from which such samples are assembled.

However, before deciding that the lack of observable fluctuations is a proof that there is no variation in the properties of individual atoms, it is necessary to estimate how large such fluctuations might be expected to be. The trouble with the simple argument given above is that appreciable fluctuations in the properties of a macroscopic sample result only when two conditions are fulfilled. First, of course, there must be an appreciable variation in some property of the microscopic building blocks; in addition, however, the number of microscopic objects in the macrosample must be reasonably small. Otherwise, the probability is overwhelming that one will measure something very close to the average sample.* The immense value of Avogadro's number implies that no fluctuation could be observed even if some of the molecules differed from the majority. The simple argument for identity from the lack of apparent fluctuation therefore fails.

Another argument for the identity of atoms depends on the natural occurrence of crystals with their smooth faces, well-defined cleavage planes, and characteristic symmetry properties. Although it is conceivable that the properties of an amorphous substance might reflect a statistical average, it seems unlikely that the very precise symmetry properties of crystals should be a consequence of any averaging process. It is tempting to attribute them instead to the identity of the constituent atoms. Indeed, the similarity of all the crystals of a given chemical compound does

---

* The fluctuation problem is discussed in the following chapter.

imply something about the likeness of the chemical constituents. However, it is not obvious that the masses or the radii are the principal factors in determining the crystal form, and more convincing evidence is needed before it can be decided what properties, if any, are necessarily identical among all the atoms of a given element found in a crystal. This assertion is borne out by the fact that different isotopes of the same element can occur throughout a crystal without disturbing the crystal stucture. Hence the mass cannot be a crucial factor.

Even according to a simple building-block view of the construction of crystals, the fact that large crystals are set in the same symmetry patterns as small ones does not necessarily prove that the basic building blocks are individual atoms. The building blocks might be larger aggregates somehow stabilized by internal forces which require the presence of a definite amount of material. Or the crystal structure might be determined by a particular geometric arrangement of atoms, rather than by the detailed structure of each one.

These thoughts about the constitution of crystals suggest similar questions about possible internal structure of atoms themselves. During most of the nineteenth century, however, such thoughts could take only the form of speculation. There was as yet no evidence for the existence of any subatomic particles. The atoms themselves had been introduced for the practical purposes of chemical construction and were viewed as indestructible elements from which more complex entities might be constructed. A considerable success was achieved from this viewpoint, especially in describing phenomena which involve averages over large numbers of atoms or molecules. These phenomena form the subject matter of the next chapter. The investigation of the atomic interior is deferred until Chapter 3.

REFERENCES

1. S. E. Virgo, *Science Progress* **108,** 634 (1933).
2. H. Helmholtz, *Journal of the Chemical Society* **39,** 277 (1881).
3. R. A. Millikan, *Electrons (Plus and Minus), Protons, Photons, Neutrons, Mesotrons and Cosmic Rays*, Revised Ed. Chicago: Univ. of Chicago Press, 1947.
4. J. Perrin, *Atoms*. London: Constable and Co., Ltd., 1920.

CHAPTER 2

SOME SUCCESSES AND FAILURES
OF NINETEENTH CENTURY ATOMISM

1. Introduction. In the 19th century the most successful application of atomic ideas to the description of the physical properties of matter was embodied in the kinetic theory of gases and its ramifications into statistical mechanics. Relatively little can be said about solids or liquids on a comparable basis. This chapter is built, therefore, largely around the kinetic theory approach to the description of gases, although many of the results turn out to have a more general applicability.

The properties of gases which kinetic theory most successfully explains depend on the existence of atoms and molecules but are largely insensitive to any internal structure of the atoms. Often a rigid-sphere model suffices, at least for a qualitative description. The fact that a large body of phenomena can be described on this basis was responsible, in good part, for the general acceptance of the atomic hypothesis at the end of the nineteenth century. The same fact, however, limits the extent to which these phenomena can contribute to a real understanding of the atom. Since the latter is our primary interest, we shall not attempt to give here a comprehensive exposition of kinetic theory. Furthermore, from our point of view the failures of the theory are almost as interesting as its successes.

Kinetic theory was developed to a high degree before its conception of the nature of the gaseous state received any direct experimental verification. The first such verification was achieved in 1911 by L. Dunoyer [1]; his experiment is shown schematically in Fig. 2-1. Sodium metal was placed in the bottom of an evacuated tube which contained two partitions with small holes in them. The metal was heated until it vaporized. After some time Dunoyer observed at the end of the tube a sharp image of the second hole. This result indicated that almost all the atoms had traveled from the source along straight-line paths and had experienced few collisions.

While Dunoyer's experiment confirmed the basic ideas of kinetic theory, it did not yield any determination of the velocities of the atoms. The velocities were first measured

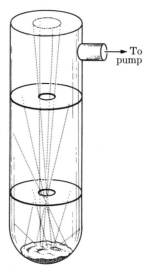

FIG. 2-1. Dunoyer's experiment.

by Stern, with a technique to be described in Section 5 of the present chapter.

2. Virial theorems and equations of state. The familiar elementary derivation of the ideal gas law from kinetic theory is based on consideration of the momentum transfer in collisions of the molecules with the walls. An instructive alternative derivation of the same result proceeds by way of the virial theorem, obtained from Newton's law,

$$m\ddot{\mathbf{r}} = \mathbf{F}, \qquad (2\text{–}1)$$

by forming the scalar product of each side with the displacement vector $\mathbf{r}$ and integrating between two times, say 0 and t. Making use of the relation

$$\mathbf{r} \cdot \ddot{\mathbf{r}} = \frac{d}{dt}(\mathbf{r} \cdot \dot{\mathbf{r}}) - (\dot{\mathbf{r}})^2, \qquad (2\text{–}2)$$

one obtains

$$m\mathbf{r} \cdot \dot{\mathbf{r}}\big|_0^t = \overline{(mv^2 + \mathbf{r} \cdot \mathbf{F})}t, \qquad (2\text{–}3)$$

where the bar indicates a time average.

For motions which are restricted in an appropriate manner, such as those of the gas particles inside a closed container, neither the displacement vector nor the velocity can exceed some maximum value; the left side of Eq. (2–3) is, therefore, bounded.* It follows that the time average of the quantity $mv^2 + \mathbf{r} \cdot \mathbf{F}$ on the right side must be zero, for otherwise the right side would increase without limit. The result,

$$\overline{mv^2} = -\overline{\mathbf{r} \cdot \mathbf{F}}, \qquad (2\text{–}4)$$

is the statement of the virial theorem.

In applying Eq. (2–4) to a gaseous system, it must be remembered that $\mathbf{F}$ contains all the forces, including those exerted by the walls of the enclosure as well as the random fluctuating forces of interaction between the molecules. The virial theorem therefore provides an opportunity for discussing the gas laws on the basis of the molecular hypothesis in a quite general

---

* This argument is, perhaps, not entirely convincing for gases in a container because, although the displacement vector is obviously restricted, it is not clear what limits the velocity; indeed, the velocity of an individual molecule does sometimes become extremely large. If, however, the energy of the gas contained in a given volume is bounded, the maximum velocity must be restricted also. The boundedness of the left side of Eq. (2–3) will be invoked either for motions in which the velocity is definitely limited because of the nature of the problem, or, in the particular case of gases, only when averaged over many molecules. In such cases the assumption of an upper bound is legitimate.

way. In such a discussion one is not interested in the motion of a single molecule, but only in averages over many molecules. Therefore, in Eq. (2–4) we perform, in addition to the time average, a summation over all the molecules, obtaining

$$N\overline{mv^2} = -\sum_{i=1}^{N} \overline{\mathbf{r}_i \cdot \mathbf{F}_i}, \tag{2–5}$$

where N is the total number of molecules. Equation (2–5) is known as Clausius' virial theorem, and the right side is called the virial. The left side is twice the translational kinetic energy of the molecules, and is related to the absolute temperature via Boltzmann's constant. (See Section 6.) Hence the equation can be written as

$$-\sum \overline{\mathbf{r}_i \cdot \mathbf{F}_i} = 3NkT. \tag{2–6}$$

To obtain an equation of state it is necessary to evaluate the virial from appropriate assumptions about the forces. The case of a perfect gas is the simplest example of this procedure. Since the molecules are assumed not to interact with one another, the virial originates entirely from the forces of the walls. For convenience we put the gas in a rectangular box with sides X, Y, Z, and choose a coordinate system with its origin at one corner and axes parallel to the edges. The force of any wall on a molecule can be resolved into a normal and a tangential component, $\mathbf{F} = \mathbf{F}_\perp + \mathbf{F}_{||}$. For each of the three walls which meet at the origin, $\mathbf{r} \cdot \mathbf{F}_\perp = 0$. Since $\mathbf{F}_{||}$ depends on the direction of impact, which is random, its component in a fixed direction (that of $\mathbf{r}$) must vanish on the average. It follows that these three sides contribute nothing to the virial. Consider now one of the other three sides, for example the top. There the vector $\mathbf{r}$ has the form

$$\mathbf{r} = Z\mathbf{k} + \boldsymbol{\rho},$$

where $\mathbf{k}$ is a unit vector in the positive z-direction and $\boldsymbol{\rho}$ a vector parallel to the xy-plane. Hence

$$\mathbf{r} \cdot \mathbf{F} = ZF_z + \boldsymbol{\rho} \cdot \mathbf{F}_{||}.$$

Again the term in $\mathbf{F}_{||}$ vanishes on the average, and the contribution to the virial from the top side is therefore

$$-\sum \overline{\mathbf{r}_i \cdot \mathbf{F}_i} = -Z \sum_i \overline{F}_{iz}.$$

But $\sum_i \overline{F}_{iz}$ at the top wall is the time-averaged force exerted by the wall on all the molecules. It is therefore the product of the pressure, p, and the area of the wall, XY, and is negative in sign. Thus

$$Z\sum \overline{F}_{iz} = Z(-pXY) = -pV. \tag{2–7}$$

Each of the other far walls contributes an equal amount. Hence, Eq. (2–6)
gives

$$3NkT = -\sum \mathbf{r}_i \cdot \mathbf{F}_i = 3pV, \qquad (2\text{–}8)$$

which is the ideal gas law.

The derivation of an equation of state by means of the virial theorem
is quite general. By evaluating the virial under more realistic assumptions
about the forces, one can derive van der Waals' equation, or even more
accurate corrections to the ideal gas law. (See, for example, Problem 2–1.)

The intermolecular forces can reasonably be assumed to arise from the
interaction between pairs of molecules; in other words, the force between
any two molecules is not changed by the presence of a third. We denote
by $\mathbf{F}_{ij}$ the force on molecule i caused by the presence of molecule j. The
total force on i is then

$$\mathbf{F}_i = \sum_j \mathbf{F}_{ij}. \qquad (2\text{–}9)$$

The force $\mathbf{F}_{ij}$, if it depends only on the separation r_{ij} of the molecules,
must be derivable from a scalar potential, that is,

$$\mathbf{F}_{ij} = -\nabla_i U(r_{ij}). \qquad (2\text{–}10)$$

Equation (2–10) shows that evaluation of the virial gives an accounting
of the potential energy effects. The significance of the virial theorem,
Eq. (2–4), can therefore be restated: the theorem relates the mean kinetic
energy of the molecules to the mean potential energy. When the kinetic
energies are translated into temperatures and the potential energy effects
are expressed in terms of volume and pressure (and sometimes also temperature) the result is an equation of state.

An example of the calculation involved in the evaluation of the virial
is furnished by the case of a single particle acted on by an attractive
central force of magnitude $F = Ar^{n-1}$. Equation (2–4) becomes for
this case

$$\overline{mv^2} = A\overline{r^n},$$

whereas the potential energy is

$$U = \frac{A}{n} r^n. \qquad (2\text{–}11)$$

It follows that

$$\overline{mv^2} = n\overline{U}, \qquad (2\text{–}12)$$

i e , the mean kinetic energy is $n/2$ times the mean potential energy.
(The zero of potential energy is taken at the origin for positive n, and at
infinity for negative n.) For example, in the harmonic oscillator, with

$U = \frac{1}{2}\kappa r^2$, the average kinetic and potential energies are equal. Another very important case is motion in an inverse-square force field, for which $n = -1$. The virial theorem states that in such a motion,

$$\overline{\frac{mv^2}{2}} = -\frac{\overline{U}}{2}. \tag{2–13}$$

The first of these examples is important because any system executing small vibrations is essentially an harmonic oscillator. The second example supplies information useful in the theory of the hydrogen atom, as well as in planetary motion.

3. Random walks and Brownian motion. When two gas molecules collide, their paths are abruptly changed; between collisions, the molecules follow straight-line paths. A good introduction to the study of such motions is provided by the problem of a two-dimensional random walk. A man starts from an arbitrary point and walks a distance L; he then turns through a random angle, and repeats the process again and again until he has walked N distances L, each in a random direction. The total distance traveled in the x-direction is

$$x = L \sum_{i=1}^{N} \cos \theta_i,$$

where θ_i is the angle between the ith path and the x-axis. If the same sequence is repeated many times the average x-displacement is

$$\overline{x} = L \sum_{i=1}^{N} \overline{\cos \theta_i}.$$

However, since the values of θ_i are distributed at random, it follows that $\overline{\cos \theta_i} = 0$, and $\overline{x} = 0$. (By symmetry, $\overline{y} = 0$ also.)

The square of the displacement behaves quite differently:

$$x^2 = L^2 \left(\sum_{i=1}^{N} \cos \theta_i \right)^2 = L^2 \left(\sum_{1}^{N} \cos^2 \theta_i + 2 \sum_{i \neq j} \cos \theta_i \cos \theta_j \right). \tag{2–14}$$

Since $\overline{\cos^2 \theta} = \frac{1}{2}$ and $\overline{\cos \theta_i \cos \theta_j} = 0$, it follows that $\overline{x^2} = L^2 N/2$ and $\overline{r^2} = \overline{x^2} + \overline{y^2} = L^2 N$. Although the mean displacement after the random walk is zero, the mean square displacement is not zero: it is proportional to the number of steps and to the square of the length of each step.

A similar behavior is found in three dimensions. For random paths in three dimensions, $\overline{\cos^2 \theta} = \frac{1}{3}$; hence $\overline{x^2} = \overline{y^2} = \overline{z^2} = \frac{1}{3}L^2 N$, and $\overline{r^2} = L^2 N$, just as in the two-dimensional case. If the motion takes place at a fixed speed v, then $NL = vt$ and $\overline{r^2} = Lvt$: the mean square displacement increases linearly with time.

The simple random walk cannot be an accurate model for the motion of a gas molecule. Certainly, the free paths between collisions in a gas are not of equal length. However, the linear increase of mean square deviations with the number of events N is a general property of random sequences, as we shall find in Section 4.

A very realistic representation for the kinetic theory picture of molecules in a gas is furnished by the motion of microscopic particles in a suspension. If a few molecules in a gas were made visible, the paths of these molecules should resemble the Brownian motions seen, for example, in Perrin's experiments described in Chapter 1. We therefore consider the Brownian motions and calculate the mean square displacement for Perrin's man-made molecules. The general result was established by Einstein [2] and independently by Smoluchowski [3] in 1905.

For bodies moving in a viscous fluid, the computation of $\overline{r^2}$ can be abbreviated by making use of an argument due to Langevin [4]. The forces acting on the body are separated into the form

$$\mathbf{F} = -\frac{1}{\beta}\frac{d\mathbf{r}}{dt} + \mathbf{f}_0. \qquad (2\text{-}15)$$

The first term in (2–15) represents the viscous drag, assumed to be proportional to the velocity. From a microscopic point of view, when a particle is in motion the random bombardment of molecules impinging upon it is modified. There are more collisions on the side of the molecule in its direction of motion than on the other side, and these impacts, on the average, tend to decrease the molecule's momentum. The effect is equivalent to an additional force directed oppositely to the motion. The amount of viscous drag depends, of course, upon the nature of the medium and also on the size and shape of the particle. In the special case of spheres of sufficient size, the coefficient β is given by Stokes' law:

$$\frac{1}{\beta} = 6\pi\eta a, \qquad (2\text{-}16)$$

where η is the viscosity and a the radius of the sphere. In general, it is not necessary to specify the value of β other than to assert that it is a constant for a given medium in thermal equilibrium and for a particular kind of particle moving through that medium.

When the force is decomposed according to (2–15), the term $\overline{\mathbf{r}\cdot\mathbf{F}t}$ which appears in the virial theorem becomes

$$\overline{\mathbf{r}\cdot\mathbf{F}t} = \overline{\mathbf{r}\cdot\mathbf{f}_0 t} - \frac{1}{2\beta}r^2\Big|_0^t. \qquad (2\text{-}17)$$

The term in $\mathbf{f}_0$ represents the random forces which an individual molecule would experience if it were standing still. These forces, when averaged over time, must cancel. The second term on the right becomes simple when averaged over a series of particles; this procedure must be carried out in addition to the time average which has already been performed. (The same result could be achieved by averaging over a sequence of trials in which a single particle is watched many times.) We shall symbolize the average over many particles with curly brackets: { }. In this notation, Eq. (2–17) is

$$\overline{\{\mathbf{r} \cdot \mathbf{F}\}t} = -\frac{1}{2\beta} \{r^2\}. \tag{2–18}$$

From the virial theorem one would expect that

$$\overline{\{mv^2\}t} = -\overline{\{\mathbf{r} \cdot \mathbf{F}\}t} = \frac{1}{2\beta} \{r^2\},$$

or

$$\{r^2\} = 2\beta\overline{\{mv^2\}}t. \tag{2–19}$$

For long times this result is indeed correct. Nevertheless, the application here of the virial theorem of the last section is not strictly justified, because the conditions under which the theorem was derived are not satisfied by the unbounded motion now under discussion. In order to be somewhat more rigorous and to establish the limitations of the result (2–19), we should return to Eq. (2–3). Introducing (2–18) into that equation gives

$$\{m\mathbf{r} \cdot \dot{\mathbf{r}}|_0^t\} = \overline{\{mv^2 + \mathbf{r} \cdot \mathbf{F}\}t} = \overline{\{mv^2\}t} - \frac{1}{2\beta} \{r^2\}, \tag{2–20}$$

which leads to a simple first-order differential equation for the mean square displacement of particles:

$$\frac{m}{2} \frac{d}{dt} \{r^2\} + \frac{1}{2\beta} \{r^2\} = \overline{\{mv^2\}}t + \frac{m}{2} \frac{d}{dt} \{r^2\}\Big|_{t=0}. \tag{2–21}$$

This equation can be used to reexamine the tentative result (2–19). It is apparent that (2–19) is completely correct only when the initial rate of increase of the mean square displacement is the same as the equilibrium rate of increase. The general result is, however, easily obtained by solving the differential equation. The solution is

$$\{r^2\} = \overline{\{2v^2\}}\tau t + \left[\frac{d\{r^2\}}{dt}\Big|_{t=0} - 2\{v^2\}\tau\right]\tau(1 - e^{-t/\tau}), \tag{2–22}$$

where

$$\tau = \beta m.$$

When $t \gg \tau$, the factor $1 - e^{-t/\tau}$ becomes unity, and the second term on the right-hand side of Eq. (2–22) approaches a constant. The right-hand side is then dominated by the term linear in t, and the solution asymptotically approaches (2–19). It may be noted that this result shows the same features as the simple random-flights problem. βm is a characteristic time; consequently $L = \beta m v$ is a characteristic distance, essentially the mean distance in which viscous drag stops a suspended particle. With $vt/L = t/\tau = N$, the number of flights, it follows that $\overline{r^2} = 2L^2 N$, which may be compared to the result $\overline{r^2} = L^2 N$ obtained on the simple random-walk model. Since the difference between $\bar{v}^2$ and $\overline{v^2}$ has been neglected and the interpretation of L is hardly exact, the agreement between the two results is as good as can be expected.

The random motion of the molecules of a gas, or of the particles in a suspension, is responsible for the diffusion which takes place whenever the concentration is nonuniform. The diffusion process is more conveniently described by considering the average behavior of the concentration of particles than by tracing the details of the mean displacement of individual particles. The net flow of particles across any surface in a gas or fluid must vanish if conditions (temperature, composition, density) are the same on both sides of the boundary. On the other hand, in a distribution with varying density a flow of particles is to be expected in the direction of the negative density gradient. The net flow per unit area and unit time caused by diffusion can be written as

$$\mathfrak{F} = -D \, \nabla n, \qquad (2\text{--}23)$$

where D has the dimension of area/time and is called the diffusion constant, and n is the number density or concentration of the particles. If diffusion alone acts, the number of particles flowing out of a unit volume is $\nabla \cdot \mathfrak{F}$, and conservation of particles requires that $\nabla \cdot \mathfrak{F} + \partial n/\partial t = 0$ in the absence of sources. Substitution of $\mathfrak{F}$ from Eq. (2–23) yields the diffusion equation

$$-\nabla \cdot (D \, \nabla n) + \frac{\partial n}{\partial t} = 0. \qquad (2\text{--}24)$$

For dilute suspensions the coefficient D depends only on the fluid in which the particles are suspended; if the fluid is uniform, (2–24) becomes

$$D \, \nabla^2 n = \partial n/\partial t. \qquad (2\text{--}25)$$

Equation (2–25) can be used to compute the mean square displacement of a group of particles. Multiplying by r^2 and integrating over all space gives:

$$D \int r^2 \, \nabla^2 n \, dV = \int r^2 \frac{\partial n}{\partial t} \, dV. \qquad (2\text{--}26)$$

The left-hand side of (2–26) can be transformed by means of Green's theorem:

$$\int r^2\, \nabla^2 n\, dV = \int n\, \nabla^2(r^2)\, dV + \int [r^2\, \nabla n - n\, \nabla(r^2)] \cdot d\mathbf{A}. \qquad (2\text{--}27)$$

The surface integrals in (2–27) vanish as long as n and ∇n decrease sufficiently rapidly at infinity, which is always the case in a problem of physical interest. Since $\nabla^2(r^2) = 6$, the remaining volume integral is just six times the total number of particles, and the left-hand side of (2–26) has the value $6ND$. On the right-hand side, the order of the time derivative and space integration can be reversed (subject to the usual mathematical conditions); the result is the time derivative of the mean square displacement,

$$\frac{\partial}{\partial t} \int r^2 n\, dV = N\, \frac{\partial}{\partial t}\, \overline{r^2}. \qquad (2\text{--}28)$$

Consequently Eq. (2–26) becomes, after the time integral is taken,

$$\overline{r^2} = 6Dt. \qquad (2\text{--}29)$$

Comparison of (2–29) with (2–19) yields an evaluation of the diffusion coefficient, D, in terms of the mean square displacement of individual particles. The two points of view, random flights and diffusion, are thus united. The result is

$$D = \tfrac{1}{3}\beta \overline{mv^2}. \qquad (2\text{--}30)$$

The diffusion treatment and the study of random flights not only agree in giving the same behavior for the mean square displacement, but also both predict a Gaussian distribution in the positions of particles which diffuse away from a given point. This result is most easily established from the solution of the diffusion equation, but it can also be obtained directly from the analysis of a large number of random flights. The latter analysis was carried out by Lord Rayleigh.

When, in addition to diffusion by random motions, systematic forces are at work, (2–23) no longer represents the net flow. For example, in a gravitational field a downward drift with average velocity $\bar{v} = \beta mg$ (m is the effective mass in the presence of the buoyant force) leads to an additional term $n\bar{v} = \beta mgn$. Equilibrium is then given by $-D\,(dn/dz) = \beta mgn$. This equilibrium must lead to the law of the isothermal atmosphere; it is therefore interesting to make a comparison with the results established in Chapter 1. In fact one can in this fashion obtain another expression for the diffusion constant. Specifically,

$$D\, dn + \beta mgn\, dz = 0$$

must be the same as Eq. (1–9), namely, $V\,dp + N_0 mg\,dz = 0$. Since n and p are proportional to each other, it follows that

$$D = \beta\,\frac{RT}{N_0} = \beta kT. \tag{2-31}$$

Equating the two expressions for D, (2–30) and (2–31), gives

$$\tfrac{1}{2}\overline{mv^2} = \tfrac{3}{2}kT, \tag{2-32}$$

the standard relation between mean translational energy and temperature.

Finally, use of the relation (2–32) allows us to rewrite the expression (2–19) for the mean square displacement as follows:

$$\overline{r^2} = 6\beta kTt = 6\beta\left(\frac{R}{N_0}\right)Tt. \tag{2-33}$$

Thus, a measurement of $\overline{r^2}$ in the Brownian motion yields another determination of Avogadro's number. Such measurements were carried out by Perrin and the resulting value of N_0 agreed, within the rather sizable error, with the values obtained in the other determinations described in Chapter 1.

4. Fluctuation phenomena and distributions. The Brownian motion illustrates an important feature of phenomena which involve a completely random element: if a series of events are statistically independent, the mean square fluctuation is proportional to the mean number of events. In the Brownian motion, $\overline{x^2}$ is proportional to t, which is a measure of the mean number of random flights. We shall derive the general law with the help of another example, which is useful in introducing the ideas of statistical mechanics.

Suppose that N beads are thrown at random into B boxes. The chance that l specified beads land in a given box is $(1/B)^l$. The chance that the remaining $N - l$ are absent is $(1 - 1/B)^{N-l}$; hence, the probability that l *particular* beads (and only those) are present in the box is $(1 - 1/B)^{N-l}(1/B)^l$. The probability $P(l, N)$ that exactly l beads be in the box (without regard to their identity) is obtained from this expression by multiplying by the number of ways of choosing l out of N objects. Calling the latter number $C(l, N)$, we have

$$P(l, N) = C(l, N)\left(1 - \frac{1}{B}\right)^{N-l}\left(\frac{1}{B}\right)^l; \tag{2-34}$$

$C(l, N)$ is just the binomial coefficient

$$C(l, N) = \frac{N!}{l!(N - l)!}. \tag{2-35}$$

From this remark it is easy to find the weighted sums defined by

$$\overline{l^k} = \sum_{l=0}^{N} l^k P(l, N).$$

For example,

$$\overline{l^0} = \sum P(l, N) = \sum C(l, N) \left(\frac{1}{B}\right)^l \left(1 - \frac{1}{B}\right)^{N-l}$$

$$= \left[\frac{1}{B} + \left(1 - \frac{1}{B}\right)\right]^N = 1,$$

and using the identity

$$x \frac{d}{dx} (x^l) = l x^l,$$

one finds

$$\overline{l} = \sum l C(l, N) \left(\frac{1}{B}\right)^l \left(1 - \frac{1}{B}\right)^{N-l}$$

$$= \left\{ x \frac{d}{dx} \sum C(l, N) x^l \left(1 - \frac{1}{B}\right)^{N-l} \right\}_{x = 1/B}$$

$$= \left\{ x \frac{d}{dx} \left(x + 1 - \frac{1}{B}\right)^N \right\}_{x = 1/B} = \frac{N}{B}. \qquad (2\text{--}36)$$

In the same way one derives the result

$$\overline{l^2} = \frac{N}{B} + \frac{N(N-1)}{B^2},$$

which implies

$$\overline{l^2} - \overline{l}^2 = \overline{l} \left(1 - \frac{1}{B}\right) \approx \overline{l}. \qquad (2\text{--}37)$$

If the number of boxes is large, the approximation embodied in the last expression is very good.

The quantity $\overline{l}$ is the average number of beads in a box, and $\Delta l = l - \overline{l}$ is the deviation from this average number. Over a large number of trials the average deviation is of course zero; however, the average square deviation is a measure of the degree of fluctuation. Its value is

$$\overline{(\Delta l)^2} = \overline{l^2 - 2l\overline{l} + \overline{l}^2} = \overline{l^2} - \overline{l}^2. \qquad (2\text{--}38)$$

For the case of statistical independence, Eq. (2–37) thus asserts that

$$\overline{(\Delta l)^2} \approx \overline{l}, \qquad (2\text{--}39)$$

a result important in the statistical analysis of data.

Frequently, the study of fluctuations can be used to measure the size of the basic unit involved. An example is the idealized experiment in which a large number, N, of identical electric charges, e, are thrown at random into B bins ($B \gg 1$). The mean square fluctuation of the charge found in one bin is then

$$\overline{(\Delta Q)^2} = \overline{Q^2} - \overline{Q}^2 = e^2\,\overline{(\Delta l)^2} \approx e^2\overline{l} = e\overline{Q}. \qquad (2\text{-}40)$$

Therefore, the unit charge is determined by the relative fluctuation times the average charge,

$$e = \left(\frac{\overline{(\Delta Q)^2}}{\overline{Q}^2}\right)\overline{Q}. \qquad (2\text{-}41)$$

By measuring the charge passed in an electron tube in fixed time intervals, such a situation can be approximately realized. The charge on the electron has been determined by this method to about one-percent accuracy. (The actual techniques and their analysis are not quite so simple. See, for example, Becker, Vol. II [5].)

The problem of distributing beads at random in a number of boxes can be used to illustrate other questions pertinent to statistical mechanics. For example, we could ask not only for the mean number of beads, but also for the most probable number to be found in any box, i.e., the value of l for which $P(l, N)$ (Eq. 2–34) is a maximum. This question is easily answered if the important values of l are substantially larger than one; l can then be considered a continuous variable. It is easiest to maximize $\ln P$ rather than P itself; differentiating the logarithm of (2–34) and using the approximate relation

$$\frac{d}{dl}\,(\ln l!) \approx \ln l \qquad (2\text{-}42)$$

valid for large l,* one obtains

$$\frac{d}{dl} \ln P(l, N) \approx -\ln l + \ln (N - l) + \ln\left(\frac{1}{B}\right) - \ln\left(1 - \frac{1}{B}\right). \qquad (2\text{-}43)$$

Setting this expression equal to zero determines l_P, the value of l for the most probable distribution. To within the approximation made, the result is

$$l_P = \frac{N}{B}. \qquad (2\text{-}44)$$

---

* Equation (2–42) can be "derived" as follows: $(d/dl) \ln l! \approx \ln l! - \ln (l - 1)! = \ln l$. The approximation involved is the same as that which leads to Stirling's formula for the factorial.

That is, the most probable value for the number of beads in a box is exactly the same as the mean value. This result is characteristic of the kind obtained whenever one deals with large numbers of particles.

Since the mean number and the most probable number of particles expected in any single box are the same, it seems fairly obvious that the most probable distribution of beads over the whole collection of boxes should be the one in which in each box contains the mean number. This statement is, however, not equivalent to what has already been proved, and it requires an independent demonstration. The considerations thus far apply to a single box, whereas we are now interested in the joint distribution over all the boxes. An argument exactly parallel to that from which Eq. (2–34) was derived yields

$$P(l_1, l_2, \ldots, l_B; N) = \frac{N!(1/B)^N}{l_1! l_2! \cdots l_B!} \qquad (2\text{--}45)$$

as the probability of finding l_1 particles in box number 1, l_2 in number 2, etc. The most probable distribution of particles among boxes is the one for which the probability P of Eq. (2–45) is maximized as a function of all the various $l_i (i = 1, \ldots, B)$ subject to the constraint that the total number of beads must be N: $\sum_i l_i = N$. The result of this maximization (that all the l_i are equal to $\bar{l}$) is most easily demonstrated with the method of Lagrange multipliers. (The mathematical technique is described in Appendix 1.) To apply the method, one forms the quantity

$$F = \ln P(l_1, l_2, \ldots, l_B; N) + \ln A \left(\sum_i l_i - N \right), \qquad (2\text{--}46)$$

where $\ln A$ is the undetermined Lagrange multiplier. The conditions

$$\partial F / \partial l_i = 0 \qquad (2\text{--}47)$$

for all l_i determine the most probable distribution. (At this step the large-number approximation again enters.) Using the relation (2–42) one gets

$$-\ln l_i + \ln A = 0$$

or

$$l_i = A \qquad (2\text{--}48)$$

for all values of i in the most probable distribution. Because

$$N = \sum_i^B l_i = BA, \qquad (2\text{--}49)$$

the final result is

$$l_i = N/B, \qquad (2\text{--}50)$$

as expected.

Recapitulating the results of the fluctuation problem, we see that the number of particles in each box in the most probable distribution is the same as the most probable number in a single box, and is also the average number. This result could have been anticipated from the fact that the mean square fluctuation increases only linearly with the number of particles per box. The distribution in the probability of finding various numbers in a single box therefore becomes more and more sharply peaked around the mean number as the number of particles increases. In fractional terms at least, the mean and the most probable values must come together.

There is another question which can be investigated by the techniques developed above, and the answer to it is of great importance. The problem is to determine the most probable distribution of a fixed number of particles throughout a collection of boxes, when each box is characterized by a specific energy. The total energy of all the particles is a constant, E. The particles are again distributed at random; however, only those arrangements are counted which satisfy the additional condition of constraint,

$$\sum l_i E_i = E, \tag{2-51}$$

where E_i is the energy characteristic of a particle in the ith box.

The most probable distribution, subject to the condition (2–51), can again be found by the method of Lagrange multipliers. We form the quantity

$$F = \ln P + \ln A(\sum l_i - N) - \mu(\sum l_i E_i - E) \tag{2-52}$$

with P still given by Eq. (2–45), and $\ln A$ and μ the Lagrange multipliers; μ has the dimension of reciprocal energy. The maximum of F as a function of all the l_i is determined by the stationarity condition (2–47), which gives

$$-\ln l_i + \ln A - \mu E_i = 0,$$

or

$$l_i = A e^{-\mu E_i}. \tag{2-53}$$

The constants A and μ are determined, as before, from the conditions of constraint,

$$N = \sum l_i = A \sum e^{-\mu E_i}$$

and

$$E = \sum E_i l_i = A \sum E_i e^{-\mu E_i}, \tag{2-54}$$

which imply that

$$E = N \frac{\sum E_i e^{-\mu E_i}}{\sum e^{-\mu E_i}} \tag{2-55}$$

and

$$l_i = \frac{N e^{-\mu E_i}}{\sum e^{-\mu E_i}}. \tag{2-56}$$

Equation (2–55) determines μ in terms of E and N, and (2–56) gives the desired distribution. As a consequence of the constraint (2–51), the particles are not uniformly distributed among the boxes; instead, the population in the most probable distribution decreases exponentially with the energy of the state. This is a general result of far-reaching importance.

The discussion in this section has been mostly mathematical; physical applications will be considered later in the chapter. One example, however, is simple enough to serve as an introduction, and also establishes more concretely the physical significance of the Lagrange multiplier μ. Suppose the beads of the earlier discussion are actually molecules of air in an isothermal atmosphere and the boxes are volume elements in that atmosphere. Assume that the molecules are distributed at random, subject only to the conservation of energy and of total number. The validity of this assumption can be at least partially. tested by comparing the results with the law of isothermal atmospheres developed in Chapter 1.

The air molecules in the various volume elements of the atmosphere differ from each other in gravitational potential energy. For the present discussion, we assume that this is the only energy which need be taken into account. Obviously, the molecules also have a kinetic energy. However, it is assumed that the distribution in kinetic energy is independent of height. If this is the case, the energy E_i is merely

$$E_i = mgh_i. \tag{2-57}$$

This expression, when substituted into the general result (2–56), gives the distribution:

$$l_i = N \, \frac{e^{-mgh_i\mu}}{\sum e^{-mgh_i\mu}}. \tag{2-58}$$

The variation with height in Eq. (2–58) is consistent with the barometer formula (1–12) if the parameter μ of the abstract statistical formulation is identified with the reciprocal of the mean thermal energy, $(kT)^{-1}$. This result has a quite general validity.

5. The Maxwell-Boltzmann distribution. The discussion thus far has not required any consideration of the distribution in velocity of the gas molecules. Whenever the velocity or momentum appeared, it was only as a mean square. It is clear, however, that a distribution in the magnitudes of the momenta is to be expected. For even if all the molecules of a gas had the same momentum at one instant, random collisions would immediately change the situation. In thermal equilibrium the average distribution must be such that the effect of collisions is just to reproduce the same distribution. That is, as many molecules are transferred into an arbitrary momentum interval by collisions as are transferred out of the same interval in the same time. This remark formed the basis for Boltzmann's method of determining the equilibrium distribution. Boltzmann showed that, at least for certain models of molecules, there is only one distribution which reproduces itself through the collision mechanism. Maxwell obtained the same distribution by other (somewhat questionable) considerations of a statistical nature. Extensive discussions of these derivations are found in all texts on kinetic theory and will not be presented here. Instead, we shall infer the Maxwell distribution by a somewhat heuristic argument. This discussion also goes back to Boltzmann [6].

Consider a gas in a uniform force field, for example, the gravitational field near the surface of the earth. The distribution of particles in such a system depends on both position and momentum. Let $dN(x, y, z; p_x, p_y, p_z)$ denote the number of molecules in a volume dx, dy, dz centered at x, y, z, having momentum components within the interval dp_x, dp_y, dp_z of p_x, p_y, p_z. Let $n(x, y, z; p_x, p_y, p_z)$ be the corresponding density, that is,

$$dN(x, y, z; p_x, p_y, p_z) = n(x, y, z; p_x, p_y, p_z)dx\, dy\, dz\, dp_x\, dp_y\, dp_z. \qquad (2\text{-}59)$$

If the form of this distribution can be derived, the limit as the strength of the field goes to zero should give the momentum distribution for a free gas.

In the uniform field, the forces on the gas molecules are independent of height. If the temperature is uniform, it is plausible that the distribution of momenta should also be independent of the height and should depend only on the temperature.* This assumption was already made in the last section; it will be justified *post-factum*. The assumption implies that the particle density has the form

$$n(x, y, z; p_x, p_y, p_z) = F(z)G(p_x, p_y, p_z), \qquad (2\text{-}60)$$

i.e., it is the product of a function of the height and a separate function of the momenta. $F(z)$, which specifies the variation of density with height in an isothermal atmosphere, is already known. It is

$$F(z) = F_0 e^{-mgz/kT}. \qquad (2\text{-}61)$$

We seek a function G of the momenta which is consistent with both the law of atmospheres (2–61) and the conservation of energy. Such a func-

---

* When a molecule moves to a higher point, its kinetic energy decreases. Therefore one might expect the velocity distribution to shift toward lower velocities as the height increases. However, the low-velocity end of the spectrum is continually being depleted as one goes to higher elevation because molecules drop out. The total density decreases with height, but those molecules which survive have the same velocity distribution.

tion is easily found if it is assumed that the gas is so dilute that collisions can be neglected. The assumption appears to be a drastic one since, according to the Boltzmann view, it is the collisions which maintain the equilibrium distribution. After the distribution is obtained, it will be argued that the solution in the presence of collisions must be the same.

In the collision-free gas, the energy of each molecule is conserved. Hence, any molecule which has the momentum p_z at a height z will have the momentum p_z' at z', where

$$\frac{(p_z')^2}{2m} = \frac{p_z^2}{2m} + mg(z - z'), \qquad (2\text{-}62)$$

since the x- and y-components of momentum do not change. Those molecules with momenta in the interval $(p_z,\ p_z + dp_z)$ will, when they arrive at z', be found in the momentum interval $(p_z',\ p_z' + dp_z')$, where

$$p_z'\, dp_z' = p_z\, dp_z. \qquad (2\text{-}63)$$

The currents carried by the same group of particles at the two heights must be the same. Since the current density is number density times velocity, this statement implies that

$$n(z; p_z)\, \frac{p_z}{m}\, dp_z = n(z'; p_z')\, \frac{p_z'}{m}\, dp_z'. \qquad (2\text{-}64)$$

Equations (2-63) and (2-64) together imply that

$$n(z, p_z) = n(z', p_z'), \qquad (2\text{-}65)$$

i.e., the densities in the combined position-momentum space are equal at two points related by (2-62). Substituting in this equation the form (2-60) and using the relation (2-62) to eliminate z, we obtain

$$e^{p_z^2/2mkT} G(p_x, p_y, p_z) = e^{p_z'^2/2mkT} G(p_x, p_y, p_z'). \qquad (2\text{-}66)$$

The left-hand side of (2-66) is independent of p_z', while the right-hand side is independent of p_z. This is possible only if the function G is of the form

$$G(p_x, p_y, p_z) = e^{-p_z^2/2mkT} H(p_x, p_y). \qquad (2\text{-}67)$$

It is noteworthy that in the expression (2-67) the strength of the gravitational field is entirely absent. Consequently the relation remains unchanged when the field strength goes to zero. When that happens, there is no longer any preferred direction, so the dependence of G on all components of momentum must be exactly the same. The distribution in momentum space, therefore, has the form:

$$n(p_x, p_y, p_z) \, dp_x \, dp_y \, dp_z = Ce^{-(p_x^2+p_y^2+p_z^2)/2mkT} \, dp_x \, dp_y \, dp_z. \qquad (2\text{--}68)$$

On changing to spherical coordinates in momentum space, the angular integration can be carried out to give the number of molecules with momentum between p and $p + dp$,*

$$n(p) \, dp = 4\pi Ce^{-p^2/2mkT} p^2 \, dp. \qquad (2\text{--}69)$$

Either (2–68) or (2–69) (or the analogous forms expressed in terms of the velocity) is called the Maxwell distribution. As already emphasized, we have not given a rigorous derivation of the Maxwell law. However, a strong case can be made for its plausibility. In the problem of the atmosphere, we have exhibited a solution for which the momentum distribution is independent of height and is determined purely by the temperature. This is the only solution consistent with the barometer formula (2–61), which in turn follows from the ideal gas law. The solution was obtained by neglecting collisions. However, if the effect of collisions were such as to change the distribution, the barometer formula would have to be modified, and the ideal gas law could not hold in a gravitational field. If the gas law is to be maintained, the effect of collisions must be only to change which molecules have which velocities. Some of the molecules originally in a particular interval of momentum space are removed from it as a result of collisions, but an equal number replaces them, and the momentum distribution is not changed. That this indeed occurs can be verified by explicit study of the collisions, but such an argument will not be presented here.

The Maxwell distribution law has been subjected to experimental check. The most direct measurement, by means of a mechanical velocity selector, was successfully carried out only relatively recently. The technique was initiated by Stern [7] in 1920, and perfected by Zartman [8] and Ko [9].

The experiment utilized a rotating drum with a slit on one side (Fig. 2–2); the deposition of molecules passing from an oven through the slit was measured on the far side of the drum. Those molecules which pass through the slit S_3 with velocity v strike the drum at positions determined by

$$s = \frac{D}{v} \left(\frac{D}{2}\right) \omega, \qquad (2\text{--}70)$$

where ω is the angular velocity of the drum and D is its diameter. The

---

* Note that the dimensions of $n(p)$, $n(p_x, p_y, p_z)$, and $n(x, y, z; p_x, p_y, p_z)$ are all different.

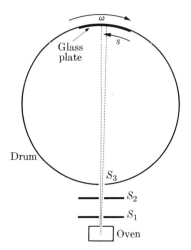

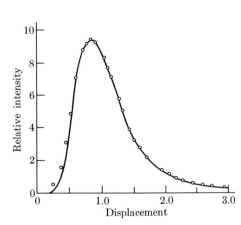

FIG. 2–2.   Rotating-drum apparatus for measurement of molecular velocity distribution [9]. The
width of slit S_3 was 0.6 mm, and
the velocity of rotation 30,000 rpm.

FIG. 2–3.   Data from rotating-drum experiment with bismuth [9]. The solid curve
is the dependence given by Eq. (2–74), predicted by the Maxwell distribution.

expression for the number of molecules that escape from the oven in unit
time with velocity v contains an additional factor of v as compared with
the velocity distribution. Hence, the number of molecules $dN(s)$ deposited
on the far wall within the interval ds at s is proportional to $v\,dn(p)$, which
can be written as

$$dN(s) \sim v\,\frac{dn(p)}{dp}\frac{dp}{ds}\,ds. \qquad (2\text{–}71)$$

From Eq. (2–70),

$$\frac{dp}{ds} = \frac{m\,D^2\omega}{2s^2}. \qquad (2\text{–}72)$$

Hence the dependence of dN/ds on s is

$$\frac{dN(s)}{ds} \sim \frac{1}{s^3}\frac{dn(p)}{dp}. \qquad (2\text{–}73)$$

If the velocity distribution in the oven is Maxwellian, the measured
intensity on the wall should have the form

$$\frac{dN(s)}{ds} \sim \frac{1}{s^5}\,e^{-a/s^2}, \qquad (2\text{–}74)$$

with

$$a = \frac{m\,D^4\omega^2}{8kT}. \qquad (2\text{–}75)$$

In any case the original distribution can be reconstructed from measurement of $s^3 \, dN(s)/ds$. The experimental results of Ko for bismuth are shown in Fig. 2–3; the agreement with the Maxwell distribution is seen to be good. The slight disagreement at the low-velocity end was explained by Ko on the assumption that the oven contained a mixture of molecules of Bi, Bi_2, and Bi_3.

6. The classical equipartition theorem. Returning to the case of the isothermal atmosphere, we can now write out the full distribution in the combined ordinary space and momentum space:

$$dN(z; p_x, p_y, p_z) = Ce^{-(mgz+p^2/2m)/kT}dx \, dy \, dz \, dp_x \, dp_y \, dp_z$$

$$= Ce^{-E/kT} \, dx \, dy \, dz \, dp_x \, dp_y \, dp_z, \qquad (2\text{–}76)$$

where $E = mgz + p^2/2m$ is the total energy of a molecule. This expression is more general than the Maxwell distribution; however, it can still be written as the product of the two factors $e^{-E/kT}$ and $dx \, dy \, dz \, dp_x dp_y \, dp_z$. As we pointed out briefly in Section 4, the exponential factor is a consequence of the constraint imposed by the conservation of energy. If a very large fraction of the energy were assigned to one molecule, many other molecules would be left with energies lower than average. Consequently even in a random distribution, if it is subject to the conservation law, there cannot be very many molecules with high energies; there must be a large bias in favor of low energies. The factor $e^{-E/kT}$, known as the Boltzmann factor, has its basis in such an argument and appears quite generally in predictions of statistical distributions.

The second factor in (2–76) is a product of the volume elements in ordinary space and momentum space. The combination of ordinary and momentum space is called "phase space." In applying the mathematical formalism of Section 4, it is clear that equal volumes in phase space constitute the physical boxes into which molecules must be distributed at random.

We are now in a position to summarize our results in the form of some principles of statistical mechanics. Although these principles will not be presented here in the most general possible way, they will be stated in somewhat greater generality than can be justified by the few examples cited.

Many systems can be described by a set of coordinates and momenta, which define a phase space. The fundamental assumption of statistical mechanics is that the a priori probabilities for occupation of two equal volumes of phase space are equal. The most probable distribution is the one which has the largest phase space; when the number of particles is large, the odds are overwhelming that the most probable distribution is the one actually observed. One must, however, keep in mind the constraints imposed by the physics of the problem. Usually the most important of these constraints is the conservation of energy, which leads in every case to a Boltzmann factor. However, other conditions of constraint may also be present, and it is even possible to discuss subsystems for which the conservation of energy is not demanded.

The problem of subsystems leads to a generalization of the statistical mechanics considered thus far. We will sketch the argument because it justifies the continued use of the Boltzmann factor even when the total energy of the system under consideration is not obviously limited.

Imagine a very large container full of gas and so well isolated from its surroundings that the energy inside must necessarily be conserved. To this container the arguments of the last few sections may be applied. Now consider a smaller region somewhere inside the large container. For the small region, which is in contact with and can exchange both energy and molecules with the rest of the container, neither the conservation of energy nor the conservation of particles holds. Nevertheless, one can be quite sure that the distributions of density and of molecular velocities in the subregion are essentially the same as those computed for the container as a whole. Indeed, the most probable distribution could not consistently be anything else. The difference between phenomena observed in a small subregion and the same phenomena averaged over the whole container lies only in the size of the fluctuations about the most probable distribution. Because energy as well as particles can flow into and out of the small subregion, there are additional fluctuations. If, however, the subregion itself contains, on the average, a sufficiently large number of molecules, the additional fluctuations cannot destroy the validity of the distribution computed for the container as a whole. The Boltzmann factor and the phase space factor must arise in a correct calculation of the distribution even in the absence of the conservation conditions, as long as one is dealing with thermal equilibrium. In subsequent volumes the Boltzmann factor will constitute a means of estimating intensities—for example, those of spectral lines or of blackbody radiation. The present brief discussion will also serve as a basis for some elementary quantum statistics when it is necessary.

If the Maxwell distribution (2–68) is integrated over all momenta, the result must be the total number of molecules per unit volume, N. The expression is the product of three identical integrals, which are of the standard Gaussian form

$$I = \int_{-\infty}^{\infty} e^{-p_x^2/2mkT}\, dp_x = (2\pi mkT)^{1/2}. \qquad (2\text{–}77)$$

Hence we have

$$C = N/(2\pi mkT)^{3/2}. \tag{2-78}$$

The mean energy is found by integrating the distribution (2-68) with the weighting factor $p^2/2m$. The result is the sum of three terms, each of the form

$$C \int_{-\infty}^{\infty} \frac{p_x^2}{2m} e^{-(p_x^2+p_y^2+p_z^2)/2mkT} dp_x\, dp_y\, dp_z. \tag{2-79}$$

This integral is the product of two like (2-77), and a third which is the derivative of (2-77) with respect to $1/kT$ and therefore has the value

$$\left(\frac{\pi m}{2}\right)^{1/2} (kT)^{3/2}. \tag{2-80}$$

It follows that (2-79) has the value $\frac{1}{2}NkT$ and the mean energy is $\frac{3}{2}NkT$. Thus we have derived from statistical mechanics the relation between mean kinetic energy and temperature which has already been used repeatedly. The result is a special case of the classical equipartition theorem. A somewhat more general illustration of the same theorem is furnished by the problem of a collection of harmonic oscillators in thermal equilibrium. The Boltzmann distribution for such a system is

$$dN = Ce^{-E/kT} dx\, dy\, dz\, dp_x\, dp_y\, dp_z, \tag{2-81}$$

where

$$E = \frac{p^2}{2m} + \tfrac{1}{2}\kappa r^2. \tag{2-82}$$

The mean energy in this distribution is the sum of six terms, all of the same form as (2-79); the result is therefore $\bar{E} = 3NkT$.* Clearly, a similar result is obtained whenever the energy is a quadratic function of coordinates and/or momenta: a contribution of $\frac{1}{2}NkT$ to the mean energy appears for each "degree of freedom," i.e. each quadratic term in the energy. Since kinetic energies are generally quadratic in the momenta, and potentials approximately quadratic for small displacements from equilibrium, the equipartition theorem has quite wide applicability.

7. Specific heats. A direct application of the ideas of kinetic theory and statistical mechanics set forth in the preceding sections is found in the problem of specific heats. The problem furnishes an excellent example of both the successes and the failures of nineteenth century atomism.

---

* The equality of mean potential and kinetic energies in this case could have been predicted from the virial theorem.

TABLE 2–1

APPROXIMATE SPECIFIC HEATS OF GASES AT CONSTANT VOLUME,
IN UNITS OF R

Type of molecule / Temperature	Monatomic	Diatomic	Linear polyatomic	Nonlinear polyatomic
Low	$\frac{3}{2}$	$\frac{3}{2}$	$\frac{3}{2}$	$\frac{3}{2}$
Moderate	$\frac{3}{2}$	$\frac{5}{2}$	$\frac{5}{2}$	$\frac{6}{2}$
High	$\frac{3}{2}$	$\frac{7}{2}$	$\frac{7}{2}, \frac{9}{2}, \ldots$	$\frac{8}{2}, \frac{10}{2}, \ldots$

If the internal energy of a gas, U, is assumed to consist entirely of translational kinetic energy, i.e.,

$$U = \tfrac{3}{2}NkT, \qquad (2\text{–}83)$$

then the molal specific heat at constant volume is

$$C_v = \tfrac{3}{2}R. \qquad (2\text{–}84)$$

At low temperatures all gases, when sufficiently dilute, are found experimentally to have specific heats close to the prediction (2–84). At higher temperatures, however, the situation becomes far more complex. The data are crudely summarized in Table 2–1. What is to be considered low, moderate, or high temperature depends upon the gas in question. The decision can be made empirically by identifying plateaus in the curves of specific heat as a function of temperature. For many gases these plateaus are very clearly defined; as an example, the specific heat of hydrogen is plotted in Fig. 2–4 against absolute temperature on a logarithic scale.

The data clearly indicate that other forms of internal energy must be present in addition to that given by Eq. (2–83). Indeed, this is to be expected. A molecule is not a mass point and may be expected to rotate; furthermore, if the molecule contains more than one atom, the atoms may vibrate with respect to one another. In a collision between two molecules, energy can be transferred between the translational, rotational, and vibrational motions; in thermal equilibrium some definite distribution of energy between the various modes is to be expected.

The fact that the specific heats tend to concentrate near integral multiples of $\tfrac{1}{2}R$ suggests an explanation in terms of the equipartition theorem. If the population of molecules obeys a Boltzmann distribution, then at equilibrium, an average energy of $\frac{1}{2}kT$ per molecule is to be associated with each quadratic term in the energy. The molal specific heat is, according to this picture, $R/2$ times the appropriate number of such quadratic terms.

A difficulty in this argument seems to occur at the outset: the very mechanism being invoked to explain the high specific heats of complicated molecules appears to spoil the agreement of the simple theory for monatomic molecules. For, even if an atom is assumed to be a rigid structure, so that internal vibration is excluded, there seems to be no reason why the atom should not rotate. Nonetheless, if the equipartition hypothesis is to have any chance of success, it is necessary to postulate that a monatomic molecule does not rotate (or at least that the rotational mode does not partake in the equipartition of energy). The only classical basis for this postulate is the fact that the moment of inertia of a single atom about its center is much smaller than that of a molecule which contains many atoms. Hence, to reach an appreciable rotational energy a single atom would require a very high angular velocity.

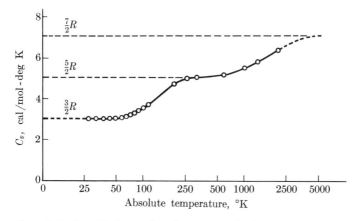

FIG. 2-4. Specific heat of hydrogen vs. absolute temperature.

If the three independent rotational degrees of freedom are included together with the translations, the predicted molal heat capacity is evidently $\frac{6}{2}R$. This is indeed the observed value for polyatomic molecules at moderate temperatures. However, it is not correct for diatomic gases like H_2 or N_2, which exhibit specific heats near $\frac{5}{2}R$. In terms of the equipartition hypothesis, this value suggests the presence of two rather than three rotational modes. The same argument invoked to account for the lack of rotational energy in monatomic gases explains the value $\frac{5}{2}R$ for the diatomic gas. In one of the three rotational modes of a diatomic molecule

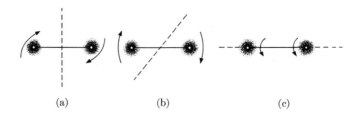

(a)   (b)   (c)

FIG. 2–5. Modes of rotation for a diatomic molecule. Mode (c) is the one which does not contribute to the specific heat.

(that in which the axis of rotation coincides with the molecular axis), both atoms rotate only about their own centers (Fig. 2–5). Hence it is at least consistent to exclude such rotations from the energy equipartition. This explanation is supported by the evidence from certain molecules which, even though they contain more than two atoms, are known from structural chemistry to be approximately linear in shape. Such substances, as indicated in Table 2–1, also exhibit specific heats consistent with two, rather than three, rotational degrees of freedom.

At higher temperatures, the specific heats of polyatomic molecules again increase. The additional energy is, presumably, vibrational. Consider, for simplicity, a diatomic molecule. The relative incompressibility of solids implies that the force between the two atoms is highly repulsive at very small separations. At very large separations, the force between the atoms is zero. Hence if there is to exist a configuration in which the atoms are bound to one another, the curve of potential energy $vs.$ separation must be qualitatively of the form shown in Fig. 2–6. The equilibrium position is at the bottom of the well ($x = x_0$). For small displacements, the potential near x_0 can be approximated by a quadratic form,

$$V = V_0 + \tfrac{1}{2}\kappa(x - x_0)^2, \qquad (2\text{--}85)$$

which leads to a harmonic vibration of frequency,

$$\omega = \left[\kappa\,\frac{m_1 + m_2}{m_1 m_2}\right]^{1/2}, \qquad (2\text{--}86)$$

where m_1 and m_2 are the masses of the two atoms in the molecule. The quantity $\mu = m_1 m_2/(m_1 + m_2)$ is the "reduced mass"; in this notation

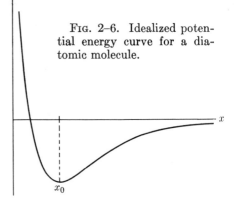

FIG. 2–6. Idealized potential energy curve for a diatomic molecule.

$\omega^2 = \kappa/\mu$, as in the vibration of a single mass on a spring of force constant κ. As already pointed out in the previous section, a Boltzmann distribution of oscillators has a mean energy kT, and therefore contributes an amount R to the molal specific heat.

The number of vibrational modes increases rapidly with the number of atoms in a molecule. The energy varies quadratically with displacement in each mode (for small displacements), and one would expect a contribution R to the specific heat from each vibrational mode in a complex molecule. The observed specific heats at high temperatures are in qualitative accord with this expectation.

A few brief remarks can also be made concerning the specific heats of solids. In a crystal each atom is bound and is not expected to exhibit any translational or rotational degrees of freedom. However, it can vibrate in any of three mutually perpendicular directions about its equilibrium position. There are, therefore, $3N_0$ vibrational degrees of freedom associated with each mole of any elementary solid. It is not necessary that the number of degrees of freedom be counted in any particular way. They may be viewed as modes of vibration of the crystal lattice as a whole, or as possible standing sound waves; in either case the total number of degrees of freedom is the same. To determine the frequency spectrum of the actual vibrations it is essential to find the simple harmonic modes of motion which are characteristic of a particular solid. If equipartition holds, however, the values of the resonant frequencies do not affect the specific heat: each vibrational mode, no matter how counted, contributes the same mean energy kT. This simple argument therefore predicts a specific heat of $3R$ (about 6 cal/mole).

The specific heats of many solids are indeed about 6 cal/mole under normal conditions. In fact, the empirical evidence was strong enough to lead Dulong and Petit to point out this regularity in the early 19th century, when it was of value as a tool in determining chemical formulas. But although there are many specific heats which agree with the law of Dulong and Petit, there are also striking exceptions. To quote an extreme case, diamond has a specific heat of only 1.46 cal/mole at room temperature.

The specific heats of solids are, like those of gases, functions of temperature. Investigation of the temperature dependence shows that the value $3R$ is often approached at high temperatures, but the specific heats fall to zero as the temperature decreases (Fig. 2–7). There is no classical explanation for this latter behavior. As in the case of gases, the criterion for what constitutes high and low temperatures is, in general, different for different solids.

A reasonably rigorous argument can be made which parallels the very qualitative discussion we have given of the classical theory of specific

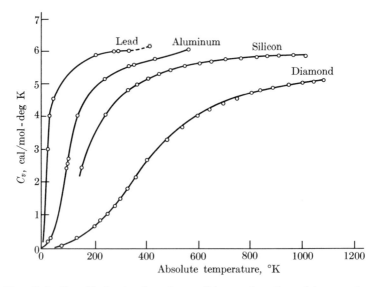

FIG. 2–7. Specific heats of various solids as a function of temperature.

heats for both gases and solids. The equipartition theorem clearly has
some relevance to the specific heats. However, there are several basic
questions which remain totally unanswered. Why are the rotational and
vibrational degrees of freedom ineffective at low temperatures? What
determines the temperature at which each mode enters? Why is there no
rotation of an atom about its center? None of these questions could be
answered without quantum ideas, and the search for the answers contributed to the advent of the quantum theory, as we shall discuss in later
volumes.

8. Transport phenomena. The derivation of the Maxwell distribution
was carried out in Section 5 without any explicit consideration of collisions. Such an approach obscures the key role played by collisions in
kinetic theory: they are the agents which establish equilibrium, starting
from any arbitrary distribution, and maintain it against fluctuations or
external disturbances. However, the form of the equilibrium distribution
does not depend on any parameters which characterize the collision process
and therefore remains unchanged even when the collision frequency goes
to zero. This circumstance makes possible the derivation in which collisions
are ignored.

In nonequilibrium phenomena, the consideration of collisions is essential.
In transport problems, for example, one is interested in the transfer of
something—be it mass, energy, or momentum—from one part of a gas
to another. The rate of transport is critically influenced by collisions;

without them no steady state could ever be established. Analysis of the transfer mechanism leads to a prediction of the viscosity and thermal conductivity of gases, which constitutes one of the major successes of kinetic theory.

The most important effects of the collisions, as far as kinetic theory is concerned, depend only on the frequency with which they occur. This frequency is determined by the density of molecules, n, and the collision cross section, σ. The probability that a molecule suffers a collision in traveling an infinitesimal distance dx is given by $\alpha\,dx$, where

$$\alpha = \sigma n. \tag{2-87}$$

If the molecules are treated as rigid spheres, σ is just the area $\pi(R_1 + R_2)^2$; with other force laws the expression for the cross section is more complicated and, in general, depends on velocity. In any case, for a given molecule the probability of traveling a distance x before colliding is

$$P(x) = e^{-\alpha x}. \tag{2-88}$$

The mean free path λ is easily calculated from (2-88):

$$\lambda = \bar{x} = \frac{\displaystyle\int_0^\infty x e^{-\alpha x}\,dx}{\displaystyle\int_0^\infty e^{-\alpha x}\,dx} = \frac{1}{\alpha}. \tag{2-89}$$

In first approximation, the entire effect of collisions is represented by the parameter λ.

As the first example of transport phenomena, we consider the problem of viscosity. Imagine a gas at constant temperature, moving in the x-direction with a velocity which increases with z: $v = v_x = f(z)$. The situation is illustrated schematically in Fig. 2–8; it can be realized experimentally by confining the gas between parallel walls, one of which is in motion. In the steady state, there exists at every point a velocity dis-

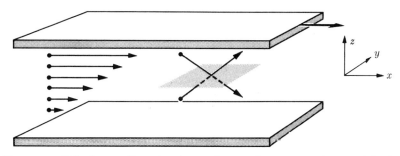

FIG. 2–8. Velocity gradient in viscous flow. The construction at right indicates the transfer of momentum by molecules crossing an area in the $x\,y$-plane.

tribution which consists of the systematic x-velocity superposed on an isotropic random motion. Since the systematic velocity is always much slower than the random motion, the latter may be expected to be little changed from the Maxwell distribution which obtains in the absence of any mass flow.

Consider a unit area in the xy-plane, at $z = z_0$. Molecules must cross this area in both directions at equal rates, since there is no net mass motion in the z-direction. However, those molecules which cross from beneath carry, on the average, a smaller x-momentum than those coming from above. Hence, there is a downward net flow of x-momentum, or equivalently, a force in the x-direction (shearing force) exerted by one layer on the next and eventually on the walls. This force is the viscous drag; the coefficient of viscosity is defined as the force per unit area and unit velocity gradient, that is,

$$F = \eta A \, dv_x/dz. \tag{2–90}$$

The x-momentum carried up across the area in unit time is the product of the rate at which molecules cross the area in that direction and the average x-momentum carried by each one. The crudest estimate for the rate of crossing is obtained from the model in which all molecules are assumed to travel with the same speed $\bar{v}$, one-third moving in each of the three coordinate directions. In such a model, the number of molecules which cross a unit area in one direction in unit time is $\frac{1}{6}n\bar{v}$. A more accurate calculation of the same quantity, which takes account of the variation of speed and of direction, is presented in Appendix 2. The result is only a change in the numerical coefficient:

$$\frac{1}{A} \frac{dN}{dt} = \frac{1}{4} \, n\bar{v}. \tag{2–91}$$

The determination of the average x-momentum carried by a molecule which crosses the area in question is not a straightforward procedure. This average momentum depends on the previous history of the molecule. It is customary to assume, in an elementary treatment, that the molecules which arrive at z_0 carry the velocity distribution characteristic of the point where their last collision took place. This assumption cannot be entirely correct. By definition, the set of molecules which collide at any point A must have the velocity distribution appropriate to that point. However, those molecules which arrive at a specified second point B form a particular subset of the ones which have collided at A: they have gone off in a particular direction and hence are more likely, on the average, to have been traveling in that same direction before the collision. Therefore the average x-velocity of these molecules must be characteristic of some point further back than A, along the same direction. This "persistence of velocity" was studied by Jeans [10] and found to be considerable. However, its effect is only to introduce a numerical factor in the final result.

We shall further assume, for simplicity, that all the molecules which cross the unit area at z_0 have traveled exactly λ since their last collision took place.* Such an assumption likewise introduces only a numerical factor. According to this model, all the molecules which cross the area from beneath had their last collision somewhere on a hemisphere of radius λ; their z-coordinate was therefore $z_0 - \lambda \cos \theta$. However, they are not equally likely to have started from all points on this hemisphere. The crossing probability is weighted by the obliquity factor $\cos \theta$ (see Appendix 2). Therefore the mean value of z from which the molecules which cross at z_0 began their most recent path is

$$z_0 - \lambda \int_{\substack{\text{hemi-}\\\text{sphere}}} d\Omega \cos^2 \theta \Big/ \int_{\substack{\text{hemi-}\\\text{sphere}}} d\Omega \cos \theta = z_0 - \tfrac{2}{3}\lambda. \qquad (2\text{-}92)$$

The mean x-momentum carried by a molecule which crosses from beneath is, then,

$$p_x(z_0 - \tfrac{2}{3}\lambda) \approx p_x(z_0) - \tfrac{2}{3}\lambda m \left.\frac{\partial v_x}{\partial z}\right|_{z=z_0} \qquad (2\text{-}93)$$

as long as the velocity gradient does not change appreciably over a mean free path. The average momentum carried by a molecule which crosses from above is evidently given by the same expression, with a plus sign instead of a minus. Hence, the net flow of momentum per unit area and unit time is,† using (2–91),

$$\frac{1}{A}\frac{dp_x}{dt} = \tfrac{1}{3}\lambda m n \bar{v} \frac{\partial v_x}{\partial z}. \qquad (2\text{-}94)$$

---

* Since λ is defined as the mean distance between collisions, it might appear that a molecule which crosses an arbitrary area has traveled, on the average, $\lambda/2$ since its last collision (and will travel another $\lambda/2$ before its next). This reasoning is, however, fallacious. The paths which cross the area do not form a random subset of all paths: the longer a path is, the more likely it is to cross, by a factor proportional to its length. With this weighting factor, the calculation of the average path which crosses the area reproduces precisely the expression (2–89). Boltzmann himself pointed out the analogy with the problem of successive tossing of a single die. The average interval between successive throws of the same number is six. However, beginning at any arbitrary time, the average interval until the next "4" is not three tosses but six, and the average interval since the last "4" is likewise six tosses.

† It is amusing to note that the same result, with the correct coefficient $\frac{1}{3}$, is obtained from the rectilinear model mentioned on p. 40. The error which the model makes in estimating the mean number of crossing molecules is precisely compensated by the error in the mean momentum carried by each molecule.

From this relation and (2–90) it follows, finally, that the viscosity coef-ficient is

$$\eta = \tfrac{1}{3}\lambda\rho\bar{v}, \qquad (2\text{–}95)$$

where $\rho = mn$ is the mass density of the gas. The result was derived by Maxwell in 1860 [11].

Equation (2–95) has a number of interesting consequences. First, since λ is inversely proportional to the density, the viscosity should be independent of density or, at constant temperature, independent of pressure. This appears at first to be an unreasonable result, since at higher density there are more molecules available to transfer momentum. However, the molecules collide and share their momentum in a shorter distance, so their efficiency in transferring momentum is correspondingly reduced. Deviations from this behavior are, of course, to be expected when the gas is so dilute that the mean free path is comparable to the dimensions of the container or so dense that it is near the point of condensation. The prediction of the theory is quite closely confirmed by experiment, as shown by the data for air given in Table 2–2. The viscosity varies by only 10% as the pressure changes over a thousandfold, and not at all between 20 and 750 mm. Such behavior would be difficult to understand on any other basis than kinetic theory.

TABLE 2–2

VISCOSITY OF AIR AT 15°C AS A FUNCTION OF PRESSURE

p, mm Hg	η, micropoises	p, mm Hg	η, micropoises
0.63	161	20.5	179
1.53	170	380	179
2.4	174	750	178

The temperature dependence of the viscosity, at constant density, comes primarily from the variation of the average speed. If the collision cross section is independent of velocity and therefore of temperature (as it is on a hard-sphere model), the dependence $\eta \sim T^{1/2}$ is predicted. Experiment shows that the viscosity does indeed increase with temperature, again contrary to intuition and unlike the viscosity of liquids. The increase is somewhat more rapid than $T^{1/2}$ (Table 2–3); the discrepancy can be largely attributed to a velocity dependence of the cross section, which is to be expected when the molecules are not treated as rigid spheres. If, for example, the force between molecules is assumed to vary as r^{-s},

TABLE 2–3

VISCOSITY OF AIR AT 1 ATM AS A FUNCTION OF TEMPERATURE

T, °C	η, micropoises	$\eta/T^{1/2}$ (absolute)	T, °C	η, micropoises	$\eta/T^{1/2}$ (absolute)
0	171	10.4	100	218	11.3
10	176	10.5	150	238	11.6
20	181	10.6	200	258	11.9
30	186	10.7	250	277	12.1
40	190	10.8	300	294	12.3
50	195	10.8	400	328	12.6
60	200	11.0	500	358	12.9

then it can be shown by dimensional arguments (see Problem 2–7) that η varies as T^α, where

$$\alpha = \frac{1}{2} + \frac{2}{s-1}. \tag{2-96}$$

Such a temperature dependence is in quite good agreement with the data for helium ($\alpha = 0.64$) and neon ($\alpha = 0.67$). For other gases a more complicated force law is required.

We turn next to the problem of thermal conductivity. It seems at first sight that this problem can be treated in precisely the same way as the viscosity. However, several new difficulties arise, which we shall discuss after first presenting the simple derivation.

Suppose the temperature of a gas (and therefore the mean energy of the molecules) increases in the z-direction. Then, by the mechanism already described, there must be a net downward flow of energy. An average molecule, starting from the point $z_0 - \frac{2}{3}\lambda$, carries the energy

$$\overline{E}\left(z_0 - \frac{2}{3}\lambda\right) = \overline{E}(z_0) - \frac{2}{3}\lambda \left.\frac{\partial \overline{E}}{\partial z}\right|_{z=z_0}. \tag{2-97}$$

This is the analog of Eq. (2–93). It follows from the same argument that H, the net energy flow per unit time across a unit area, is

$$H = -\frac{1}{3}\lambda n\bar{v}\,\frac{\partial \overline{E}}{\partial z}. \tag{2-98}$$

The thermal conductivity κ is defined as the heat flow per unit temperature gradient·

$$H = -\kappa\,\frac{\partial T}{\partial z}. \tag{2-99}$$

The last two expressions are related because

$$\frac{\partial \overline{E}}{\partial z} = \frac{\partial \overline{E}}{\partial T} \frac{\partial T}{\partial z}$$
$$= \frac{C_v}{N_0} \frac{\partial T}{\partial z},$$

(2-100)

where N_0 is Avogadro's number and C_v the molal specific heat. It follows that the conductivity is

$$\kappa = \frac{1}{3} \overline{v} \lambda C_v \frac{n}{N_0}.$$

(2-101)

The predicted conductivity is, just like the viscosity, independent of density and increases with temperature approximately as $(TC_v)^{1/2}$. The conductivity has been found experimentally to be independent of pressure down to as low as 1 cm of mercury.

On comparing Eqs. (2-101) and (2-95), one obtains the interesting relation

$$\kappa = \frac{\eta C_v}{m N_0} = \eta c_v,$$

(2-102)

where c_v is the specific heat per unit mass rather than per mole. Table 2-4 gives the data for several gases on the quantities which appear in Eq. (2-102). It can be seen that the agreement is surprisingly good. The ratio $\kappa / \eta c_v$ is somewhat larger than one but does not exceed 2.5, even though the individual quantities vary much more.

It must be pointed out, however, that the derivation of the heat conductivity has glossed over some important sources of difficulty. In the first place, if the temperature varies with z, then so do the density and the mean velocity (as well as the mean free path). The arguments which lead to Eq. (2-98) must be reexamined in the light of this new complication. Since the average upward-moving molecule started from $z_0 - \frac{2}{3}\lambda$, the first-order correction consists of calculating the factor $n\overline{v}$ at that point. If this is done, one obtains instead of (2-98) the expression*

$$H = -\frac{1}{3}\lambda \frac{\partial}{\partial z} (\overline{E} \, n\overline{v}) \bigg|_{z=z_0},$$

(2-103)

which contains the additional term

$$\frac{1}{3}\lambda \overline{E}(z_0) \frac{\partial}{\partial z} (n\overline{v}) \bigg|_{z=z_0}.$$

(2-104)

---

* The variation of λ with z is not included in this expression. With nonuniform density the distribution of free paths is not exponential, and the calculation of λ is complicated. When this factor is taken into account, an additional correction term is obtained.

TABLE 2-4

(a) THE RATIO $\kappa/\eta c_v$ FOR VARIOUS GASES AT 0°C*

Gas	$\eta \times 10^6$	$\kappa \times 10^6$	c_v cal/gm-deg	$\kappa/\eta c_v$
He	187.5	344	0.753	2.44
Ne	298.6	110.4	0.150	2.47
A	210.0	38.7	0.0763	2.42
H_2	84.0	416	2.40	2.06
N_2	166.4	56.6	0.178	1.91
O_2	191.8	57.3	0.156	1.92
H_2O (100°C)	121.5	55.1	0.366	1.24
CO_2	137.7	34.0	0.151	1.64
NH_3	91.5	51.4	0.401	1.40

* Data taken from Kennard [12].

(b) TEMPERATURE DEPENDENCE OF $\kappa/\eta c_v$ FOR H_2

T (absolute)	$\dfrac{\kappa}{\kappa_{0°C}}$	$\dfrac{\kappa/\eta c_v}{(\kappa/\eta c_v)_{0°C}}$
194.6	0.774	1.07
81.5	0.335	1.15
21.0	0.0813	1.21

This term should contribute to the conductivity. However, a further argument suggests that the additional term should vanish, for the same expression represents the net number of molecules which cross the unit area in unit time. In the definition of thermal conductivity (2–99), it is implied that there is no net mass motion; otherwise there would be a transfer of energy by convection.

However, yet another condition must be satisfied, which seems inconsistent with the constancy of $n\bar{v}$. If no mass motion is to take place, there ought to be no change in pressure with z (or equivalently, no net momentum flow across the horizontal area). The constancy of pressure implies that

$$\frac{\partial}{\partial z} \left(\overline{nv^2} \right) = 0. \qquad (2\text{--}105)$$

Equation (2–105) is clearly inconsistent with Eq. (2–104) if the velocity distribution is Maxwellian at every point, as has been tacitly assumed all along, for Eq. (2–105) requires that nT be constant, whereas Eq. (2–104) requires that $nT^{1/2}$ be constant. The conclusion is inescapable that the velocity distribution must differ from Maxwellian in an important way.

Indeed, on reconsideration it seems quite reasonable that the distribution should be non-Maxwellian. The situation is not one of equilibrium; furthermore it is not even symmetric. Since the system has a preferred direction, it would be surprising if the velocity distribution were everywhere spherically symmetric.

The more rigorous treatments of the problem begin from this point of view, writing the distribution as a Maxwell function plus an additional term [12]. The transport properties are a consequence of the additional term. The result of such analyses is still an equation of the form (2–101), but with a different constant of proportionality which brings the prediction into more satisfactory agreement with experiment. In a rigorous treatment of the viscosity it, too, is completely explained by a deviation from the Maxwell distribution.

The successful theories of viscosity and heat conduction furnished strong support for the atomic theory at the middle of the nineteenth century. The measurement of η and κ could be taken as an indication of the mean free path and thus of the molecular cross sections. These in turn give yet another measure of molecular sizes. The diameters determined in this fashion have been listed together with other estimates in Table 2–5.

TABLE 2–5

MOLECULAR DIAMETERS*

Gas	Diameter (Angstroms) as determined from		
	Viscosity	Van der Waals constant b	Density of liquid
Hydrogen	2.70	2.53	3.94
Helium	2.18	1.97	4.0
Chlorine	5.41	—	4.63
Argon	3.67	2.87	4.04
Oxygen	3.65	2.91	3.72
H_2O	4.58	—	3.76
Nitrogen	3.79	3.56	3.98
CO_2	4.58	3.42	4.06
Krypton	4.13	3.16	4.46
Xenon	4.88	3.45	4.50 *

* Data from: F. H. Newman and V. H. L. Searle, *The General Properties of Matter*, London: Edward Arnold and Co., 1948

The different determinations are in qualitative agreement, although considerable variations appear. This is hardly surprising since each experiment actually measures a different property of the molecule, each of which can be roughly identified with the macroscopic concept of size.

REFERENCES

1. L. DUNOYER, *Comptes Rendus* **152**, 592 (1911).
2. A. EINSTEIN, *Ann. der Physik* **17**, 549 (1905); **19**, 371 (1906).
3. M. SMOLUCHOWSKI, *Ann. der Physik* **21**, 756 (1906).
4. P. LANGEVIN, *Comptes Rendus* **146**, 530 (1908).
5. R. BECKER, *Theorie der Elektrizität* (Teubner Verlag, 1933), Vol. II, p. 6.
6. L. BOLTZMANN, *Wien. Ber.* **74**, 503 (1876).
7. O. STERN, *Zeitschrift für Physik* **2**, 49 (1920); **3**, 417 (1920); *Phys. Zeitsch.* **21**, 582 (1920).
8. I. F. ZARTMAN, *Phys. Rev.* **37**, 383 (1931).
9. C. C. KO, *Journal Franklin Institute* **217**, 173 (1934).
10. J. H. JEANS, *Dynamical Theory Of Gases.* Cambridge University Press, 1925 (Dover reprint, 1954).
11. J. C. MAXWELL, *Phil. Mag.* **19**, 20 (1860).
12. E. H. KENNARD, *Kinetic Theory of Gases.* New York: McGraw-Hill, 1938, pp. 165ff.

PROBLEMS

1. Suppose that the molecules of a gas are represented as rigid spheres of radius R. The force between them is then an impulsive one, which abruptly changes the momentum whenever the distance between centers of a pair of molecules reaches the value $2R$. Since this force obeys Newton's third law, the virial contains a term $\mathbf{r}_{ij} \cdot \mathbf{f}_{ij}$ during the brief time of a collision.

By averaging the impulse in a single collision and considering the frequency of collisions, show that the contribution to the virial is of the form

$$-\overline{(\Sigma \mathbf{r}_i \cdot \mathbf{f}_i)}_{\text{collision}} = \overline{\beta m v^2} \frac{NV_0}{V},$$

where N is the total number of molecules, V_0 the volume of a molecule, and V the volume of the container. Find an approximate value for the numerical coefficient β.

Suppose that in addition to the hard sphere repulsion there is an attractive potential $U(r_{ij})$, weak enough so that any increase in velocity when the molecules approach each other may be neglected. All relative separations are then equally likely (except that $r_{ij} < 2R$ is excluded). Under these assumptions show that the virial receives an additional contribution of the form

$$-\overline{(\Sigma \mathbf{r}_i \cdot \mathbf{f}_i)}_{\text{interaction}} = \frac{N^2 V_0}{V} U_0,$$

where U_0 is an appropriately averaged energy. Show that these contributions, together with that from the walls, lead to an equation of state of the form

$$\left(p + \frac{a}{V^2}\right) V = NkT \left(1 + \frac{b}{V}\right).$$

When $b/V \ll 1$, this may be written as

$$\left(p + \frac{a}{V^2}\right)(V - b) = NkT,$$

which is van der Waals' equation.

2. Consider a particle in a Brownian motion as discussed in Section 2–3, but subject to an additional constant force **F**. Show that if the particle starts at the origin its mean displacement is

$$\bar{\mathbf{r}} = \frac{\mathbf{F}}{m}\tau t + \left[\left(\frac{d\mathbf{r}}{dt}\right)_0 - \frac{F}{m}\tau\right]\tau(1 - e^{-t/\tau}).$$

Interpret the terms physically.

3. Show by the method of Lagrange multipliers that if N_1 molecules of one gas and N_2 molecules of another share the total energy E, the most probable distribution involves only one temperature. Notice that because the distributions for the two gases are independent (aside from the energy constraint), the *a priori* probability for any overall distribution is a product of the probabilities for the distribution of each gas separately.

4. The molecules of gas A can occupy with equal *a priori* probability two possible states, in one of which the energy is $2E_0$, and in the other $3E_0$. Gas B similarly has two possible states, in which the energies are E_0 and $2E_0$, respectively.

(a) A system consists of two molecules of gas A and one molecule of B; the total energy is $6E_0$. What is the most probable distribution?

(b) A system consists of 2×10^{21} molecules of gas A and 10^{21} molecules of B. The total energy is $6 \times 10^{21}E_0$. What is now the most probable distribution?

5. A particle may occupy one of three states, in which its z-component of angular momentum is 1, 0, and −1 respectively. Suppose there are N such particles and the *a priori* probabilities for the occupation of each state are equal. Find the most probable distribution, subject to the condition that the total z-angular momentum is M. If $M \ll N$, show that the result reduces to

$$N_1 = \frac{N}{3} + \frac{M}{2},$$

$$N_0 = \frac{N}{3},$$

$$N_{-1} = \frac{N}{3} - \frac{M}{2}.$$

6. The potential energy of an oscillator is given by

$$U = \tfrac{1}{2}\mu(r - r_0)^2.$$

Using the Maxwell-Boltzmann distribution, write an expression for the mean energy of a collection of such oscillators. Evaluate $\overline{U}$ and find the specific heat in the limits $r_0 \to 0$ and $r_0 \to \infty$. How large must r_0 be before $\overline{U} \approx \overline{U}(r_0 = \infty)$? Discuss the connection with diatomic molecules.

7. Suppose the force between two molecules is of the form $F = kr^{-s}$. If the viscosity is independent of density, it can depend only on the mass m of the molecules, the mean velocity $\bar{v}$, and the force constant k. Show by dimensional analysis that η must be proportional to

$$(m^{-2}\,\bar{v}^{-s+3}\,k^{-2})^{1/(s-1)}$$

and therefore that the temperature dependence of η is given by Eq. (2–96). The argument is due to Lord Rayleigh.

8. Assume that the free electrons in a metal form a "gas," with a mean free path λ determined by collisions with atoms, and that this gas is responsible for both the electrical and thermal conductivity of the metal. Assuming further that an imposed electric field $\mathbf{E}$ affects the random motions of the electron gas only slightly, construct a crude theory of the electrical conductivity. What is the ratio of thermal to electrical conductivity? (This result is called the Wiedemann-Franz law.)

CHAPTER 3

ATOMIC CONSTITUENTS AND ATOMIC MODELS

1. High vacua and new phenomena. During the latter part of the nineteenth century, progress in vacuum technique made possible the study of an entirely new class of phenomena. For the first time experiments could be carried out at pressures lower than a millionth of an atmosphere, which correspond to mean free paths of the order of a hundred centimeters at room temperature. Under such conditions the effects of random collisions are practically negligible. It therefore became possible to follow the passage of individual charged particles over well-defined paths, to accelerate them to relatively high energy, and to observe the deflections caused by electric and magnetic fields under the control of the experimenter.

Electrical discharges in gases had already been under study for some time. However, the development of improved vacuum techniques (both pumps and containing vessels) transformed a very complicated and almost uninterpretable state of affairs into one in which certain phenomena of great universality could be identified. The study of low-pressure discharges quickly led to the discovery of cathode rays, a radiation independent of the nature of the gas in the vessel; a reasonably precise identification of cathode rays was already given by Hittorf in 1869. In 1886 positively charged rays were clearly identified by Goldstein. Further progress was achieved in the work of Crookes, and in 1897 the nature of cathode rays was fully established by Thomson and others.

The investigations of gas discharges at very low pressures marked a decisive break with all earlier atomic experiments. The identification of the electron was a sharp determination: the specific charge was measured in such a way that average values, which were the characteristic of previous nineteenth-century measurements, were not involved. Each electron in the new experiments behaved in exactly the same way as all the others. Such behavior was in sharp contrast to the chaos of molecular motions involved in experiments dealing with equations of state, for example, or with specific heats. The latter experiments measured the average properties of large collections, rather than the behavior of sequences of individual particles. They were entirely macroscopic, whereas the Thomson experiments isolated the submicroscopic individual. Modern atomic physics may well be said to have started with the experiments which elucidated the nature of cathode rays.

Before turning to the details of the discovery of the electron, it may be helpful to mention some related phenomena which came under study at about the same time. Heinrich Hertz, while he was verifying Maxwell's theory of light in 1887, produced electromagnetic waves and studied their properties. In the course of this work he noticed that, under certain circumstances, ultraviolet light incident on a metallic surface induced an electrical emission; thus he discovered the photoelectric effect. The effect was studied further by Hallwachs and others before 1900, and careful experiments to establish the quantitative laws of photoelectric emission were subsequently performed (for example, by Compton and Richardson in 1912 and by Millikan in 1916). The theoretical interpretation of the photoelectric effect by Einstein in 1905 was in many ways the real beginning of the quantum theory.

In 1895 two important discoveries were made: x-rays were observed by Roentgen originating from the walls of cathode ray tubes, and radioactivity was discovered by Becquerel. Both these phenomena provided physics with new tools as well as with new problems. Projectiles were supplied with which the structure of atoms could be investigated, but the new phenomena had also to be understood and fitted into the picture of the atomic world.

Another important development which took place at about the same time was the discovery of the Zeeman effect in 1896. Zeeman found that when a magnetic field is applied to a source of electromagnetic radiation, the emitted spectral lines are split. The Zeeman effect was interpreted immediately by Lorentz as proof that the light emitted by atoms results from the accelerated motion of electrons. The specific charge of the accelerated particle could be estimated from the magnitude of the Zeeman splitting, and the value thus obtained agreed with the specific charge of cathode rays measured by Thomson.

Finally, we should mention that the investigation and systematization of atomic spectra were advancing rapidly at the end of the nineteenth century and also benefited greatly from the improvement in vacuum technique. All these developments are discussed in the next volume.

2. Gas discharges and cathode rays.

Beautiful as well as interesting phenomena occur when a reasonably large potential difference, say of the order of 1000 volts, is maintained between two electrodes in a gaseous medium. Light of various characteristic colors is emitted from the gas in the space between the electrodes. At particular pressures striations, dark spaces, and other striking effects may be observed. The physics of these phenomena is certainly not simple. Many processes are taking place simultaneously, and to extract something meaningful from such a complex situation is a difficult task. Investigation still continues in the attempt to fully understand the gas discharge.

The first constituent of the gas discharge to be clearly identified was the cathode ray. At pressures of 10^{-3} mm of mercury ($\sim 10^{-6}$ atm) or less, a phenomenon was observed and found to be independent of the nature of the gas: something was seen to propagate from the cathode in straight lines. This "something" was called the cathode ray; it was identified by the phosphorescence produced when the radiation impinged on the walls of the glass container. The straight-line propagation may be convincingly established by placing an obstacle of some characteristic shape in the path of the rays. (The Maltese cross was an early favorite for demonstration purposes.) A shadow of the obstacle is then observed on the wall; if the cathode is small enough to act approximately as a point source, the shadow is quite sharp.

The nature of cathode rays was a question of great interest in the early 1890's. They were at first believed to be a form of light, but rough estimates of their velocity showed it to be considerably less than that of light. In 1895 Perrin caught the cathode rays in a Faraday cylinder and found that the cylinder became negatively charged [1]. He then deflected the rays with a magnet; their path was bent away and the collector no longer acquired any charge. On the basis of these results, Perrin asserted that the cathode radiation was a flow of negative charge. However, the experimental arrangement was such that *any* charged particles emitted at the cathode would have been caught in the collector. Therefore it was possible that the charge which Perrin had accumulated and measured might have been carried not by the cathode rays themselves, but by some other agent which was emitted simultaneously at the cathode. Furthermore, it was argued by some critics, if the cathode rays were charged they ought to be deflected from a straight-line path by an electrostatic field as well as by a magnet. Hertz had tried in 1883 to observe such an electrostatic deflection but had obtained a null result.

On the basis of the somewhat contradictory early evidence, many investigators (particularly in Germany) became convinced that the cathode rays were some new sort of "disturbance of the aether" rather than material particles [2]. This view was supported by the observation of Lenard [3] and others that cathode rays could penetrate a considerable amount of solid matter; such behavior seemed unlikely for material particles. Lenard's data indicated that the absorption of the rays depends only on the total amount of material through which they pass, and not on the detailed nature of the medium.

3. Thomson's identification of the electron. J. J. Thomson, in a justly celebrated experiment, showed convincingly that the cathode rays do consist of a stream of negatively charged particles and determined their specific charge [4]. Thomson first repeated Perrin's experiment, taking care to ensure that everything but the cathode rays was excluded from the measuring apparatus. The results indisputably confirmed Perrin's conclusion: the charge was definitely carried by the cathode rays themselves. Thomson also explained why Hertz had been unable to observe any electrostatic deflection. The vacuum in Hertz's experiments had not been good enough to prevent the cathode rays from ionizing the gas in the container appreciably. As a result, the charge on the deflecting plates was continually leaking off and no field actually existed between them. Repeating Hertz's experiment at a lower pressure, Thomson verified that the rays were indeed deflected by an electrostatic field.

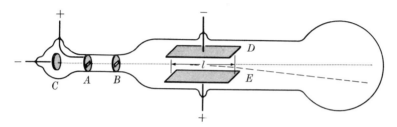

FIG. 3–1. Thomson's e/m experiment. (Source of magnetic field not shown.)

Thomson used two independent methods to determine the specific charge of the cathode rays. The better known determination was based on measurement of independent electric and magnetic deflections, using the experimental arrangement shown in Fig. 3–1. The rays from the cathode C were accelerated toward the anode A, and some of them passed through a slit in A. After going through a second slit B (to define the direction more precisely), the beam passed between the parallel deflecting plates D and E and finally struck the end of the glass tube, where it produced a narrow phosphorescent patch.

When an electric field was turned on between the plates, the position of the patch shifted. It is straightforward to calculate the deflection to be expected if the beam consists of particles of charge e, mass m, and initial velocity v. The angle at which the rays are traveling when they leave the region between the plates is given by

$$\tan \theta = \frac{eEl}{mv^2}, \qquad (3\text{–}1)$$

where E is the electric field strength and l the length of the plates. (The effects of fringing fields are neglected.) Since E and l are known, measurement of θ determines the value of the quantity e/mv^2. An additional relation is required before the specific charge e/m can be calculated. This was obtained by turning off the electric field and replacing it with an approximately uniform transverse magnetic field, occupying the same space. A sufficiently accurate expression for the magnetic deflection can be obtained very simply by noting that the force due to a magnetic field B is equal (for $v \ll c$) to that of an equivalent electric field E', where*

$$E' = \left(\frac{v}{c}\right) B. \tag{3-2}$$

The angle of magnetic deflection ϕ then follows directly from Eq. (3–1):

$$\tan \phi = \frac{eE'l}{mv^2} = \frac{eBl}{mvc}. \tag{3-3}$$

This result is only approximate because, once the beam has been deflected a little, the magnetic force changes in direction. The acceleration then has a longitudinal as well as a transverse component, and the equivalent electric field is no longer transverse. However, as long as the deflection is small, the error in Eq. (3–3) is likewise small.

Equations (3–1) and (3–3) determine both the velocity and the specific charge:

$$\frac{v}{c} = \frac{\tan \phi}{\tan \theta} \frac{E}{B}, \tag{3-4}$$

and

$$\frac{e}{m} = c^2 \frac{E \tan^2 \phi}{B^2 l \tan \theta}. \tag{3-5}$$

Thomson performed a series of experiments of this type, using tubes which contained air, hydrogen, and carbon dioxide at different pressures and cathodes made of platinum, aluminum and iron. The velocities of the rays ranged between 2.2×10^9 and 3.6×10^9 cm/sec, about 10% the velocity of light. In all cases the values obtained for e/m were between 2×10^{17} and 3×10^{17} esu/gm.

The major source of error in the experiment was the neglect of the magnetic field in the region outside the plates.† This field was opposite in direction to that in the interior; it therefore reduced the deflection of the beam, and likewise reduced the value of e/m calculated from Eq. (3–5). The currently accepted value for the specific charge is 5.27×10^{17}

---

* Gaussian units are being used. That is, electric quantities are measured in esu, magnetic quantities in emu, and the force on a charge is $\mathbf{F} = q(\mathbf{E} + \boldsymbol{v} \times \mathbf{B}/c)$. A more complete discussion of units is given in Appendix 1 of Volume 2.

† Any distribution in the velocities of the beam particles would have caused a spreading out of the observed spot and added appreciably to the error. Fortunately, in Thomson's experiment all the particles had very nearly the same velocity, since they were emitted essentially at rest and accelerated through the same potential difference.

esu/gm, so a correction for the external magnetic field would have improved the accuracy of Thomson's value. In any case, the important result of the experiment was that the specific charge was the same for all cathode rays, independently of the cathode material, the nature of the gas, and the velocity of the rays (within the limited range measured).

Thomson also obtained the value of e/m by a second method, in which the total energy transported by cathode rays in a given time was measured by calorimetry, the total charge by collection in a Faraday cylinder, and the magnetic deflection by the procedure just described. From these data the specific charge can be calculated. The measurements were, like the other ones, carried out with various cathodes and with different gases in the discharge tube; the results were again independent of these factors. Although the results showed considerably more scatter than did those in Thomson's other method, the systematic error was apparently smaller, since the calculated values of e/m were closer to the correct value. They ranged between 3×10^{17} and 9×10^{17} esu/gm.

It should be noted that Kaufmann [5] and Wiechert [6] also determined the specific charge of cathode rays at about the same time as Thomson. Kaufmann measured the magnetic deflection of the rays by a procedure similar to Thomson's. He did not measure an electric deflection, but estimated the velocity of the rays by assuming that they had all been accelerated from rest through a potential difference equal to the anode potential. This assumption neglects any energy loss caused by collisions with gas molecules, as well as the energy required to pull the electrons out of the cathode (work function). At the time, it was not known that the latter quantity is quite small. (The smallness of the collision loss was confirmed by the lack of spreading of the beam.) In point of fact the numerical result obtained by Kaufmann, $e/m = 5.58 \times 10^{17}$ esu/gm, was more accurate than Thomson's. During the following years, measurements with increased accuracy were carried out by Simon (1901), Seitz (1902–3), and Becker (1905). In 1911 Malassez obtained a result which agrees with the modern value to better than three significant figures.

Thomson's discussion of his results is so incisive and of such importance that instead of paraphrasing it we shall quote part of it:

From these determinations we see that the value of m/e is independent of the nature of the gas, and that its value $10^{-7}*$ is very small compared with the value 10^{-4}, which is the smallest value of this quantity previously known and which is the value for the hydrogen ion in electrolysis.

Thus for the carriers of the electricity in the cathode rays m/e is very small compared with its value in electrolysis. The smallness of m/e may be due to

---

* Thomson is using electromagnetic units of charge. (1 emu $= 3 \times 10^{10}$ esu.)

the smallness of m or the largeness of e, or to a combination of these two. That the carriers of the charges in the cathode rays are small compared with ordinary molecules is shown, I think, by Lenard's results as to the rate at which the brightness of the phosphorescence produced by these rays diminishes with the length of path travelled by the ray. If we regard this phosphorescence as due to the impact of the charged particles, the distance through which the rays must travel before the phosphorescence fades to a given fraction of its original intensity will be some moderate multiple of the mean free path. Now Lenard found that this distance depends solely upon the density of the medium, and not upon its chemical nature or physical state. In air at atmospheric pressure the distance was about half a centimetre, and this must be comparable with the mean free path of the carriers through air at atmospheric pressure. But the mean free path of the molecules of air is a quantity of quite a different order. The carrier, then, must be small compared with ordinary molecules.

The two fundamental points about these carriers seem to me to be (1) that these carriers are the same whatever the gas through which the discharge passes, (2) that the mean free paths depend upon nothing but the density of the medium traversed by these rays . . .

The explanation which seems to me to account in the most simple and straightforward manner for the facts is founded on a view of the constitution of the chemical elements which has been favorably entertained by many chemists: this view is that the atoms of the different chemical elements are different aggregations of atoms of the same kind. In the form in which this hypothesis was enunciated by Prout, the atoms of the different elements were hydrogen atoms; in this precise form the hypothesis is not tenable, but if we substitute for hydrogen some unknown primordial substance X, there is nothing known which is inconsistent with this hypothesis, which is one that has been recently supported by Sir Norman Lockyer for reasons derived from the study of the stellar spectra.

If, in the very intense electric field in the neighborhood of the cathode, the molecules of the gas are dissociated and are split up, not into the ordinary chemical atoms, but into these primordial atoms, which we shall for brevity call corpuscles;* and, if these corpuscles are charged with electricity and projected from the cathode by the electric field, they would behave exactly like the cathode rays. They would evidently give a value of m/e which is independent of the nature of the gas and its pressure, for the carriers are the same whatever the gas may be; again, the mean free paths of these corpuscles would depend solely upon the density of the medium through which they pass. For the molecules of the medium are composed of a number of such corpuscles separated by considerable spaces; now the collision between a single corpuscle and the molecule will not be between the corpuscles and the molecule as a whole, but between this corpuscle and the individual corpuscles which form the molecule; thus the number of collisions the particle makes as it moves through

---

* The "corpuscles" soon became known as electrons; however, Thomson and the English school tenaciously held on to the term corpuscle for considerable time.

a crowd of these molecules will be proportional, not to the number of the molecules in the crowd, but to the number of the individual corpuscles. The mean free path is inversely proportional to the number of corpuscles in unit volume; now as these corpuscles are all of the same mass, the number of corpuscles in unit volume will be proportional to the mass of unit volume, that is the mean free path will be inversely proportional to the density of the gas. We see, too, that so long as the distance between neighbouring corpuscles is large compared with the linear dimensions of a corpuscle the mean free path will be independent of the way they are arranged, provided the number in unit volume remains constant, that is the mean free path will depend only on the density of the medium traversed by the corpuscles, and will be independent of its chemical nature and physical state: this from Lenard's very remarkable measurements of the absorption of the cathode rays by various media must be a property possessed by the carriers of the charges in the cathode rays.

Thus on this view we have in the cathode rays matter in a new state, a state in which the subdivision of matter is carried very much further than in the ordinary gaseous state: a state in which all matter—that is, matter derived from different sources such as hydrogen, oxygen, etc.—is of one and the same kind; this matter being the substance from which all the chemical elements are built up.

Thomson's experiment signaled two great departures from the previous physics of the nineteenth century. First, as already remarked, a unique value for the specific charge was provided. Previous determinations by electrochemical means had been, of necessity, averages taken over very large samples. In Thomson's experiment any variation in the value of e/m would have been apparent. The fact that all the electrons landed at the same spot on the screen demonstrated their identity in a quite direct manner.

In addition, Thomson's work marked the transition between the early experiments in which the atom always acted as a whole and its internal structure played no part, and the subsequent experiments in which the atomic constituents came under scrutiny. With the identification of the electron as a fundamental constituent for atoms, Thomson initiated the study of atomic structure.*

The universality of the electron, inferred by Thomson from the results of his experiment, was supported by other evidence accumulated during the period shortly afterward. That electrons are present inside atoms themselves was strongly suggested by the Zeeman effect. Electrons were

---

* Wiechert and Kaufmann, who, as we have mentioned, performed experiments similar to Thomson's, failed to make this all-important interpretation. Kaufmann in fact concluded, from the fact that e/m was independent of the nature of the gas in the tube and the kind of cathode used, that the cathode ray particles did not come from either the gas or the metal.

also shown to be identical with the beta rays emitted in radioactive disintegration and with the particles emitted in the photoelectric effect. In each case, the proof consisted essentially in showing that the specific charge of the particles in question was the same as that of cathode rays. The specific charge of beta rays was first measured by Becquerel in 1899 and that of photoelectrons by Lenard in 1900, by deflection experiments similar to Thomson's. It rapidly became clear that the electron is indeed ubiquitous and must certainly play an essential role in any model for the construction of atoms.

The specific charge determined in Thomson's experiments was almost 2000 times greater than the largest ever obtained from electrochemical data. It followed that the electron must have either a charge many times greater than that of any ion, or a mass about 1/2000th of the mass of the hydrogen atom, or perhaps some combination of unusually small mass with unusually great charge. It is interesting to note that Thomson at first believed the last alternative to be the correct one. The selection already quoted from his paper contains arguments for the smallness of m. However, a later paragraph in the same paper reads:

The smallness of the value of m/e is, I think, due to the largeness of e as well as the smallness of m. There seems to me to be some evidence that the charges carried by the corpuscles in the atom are large compared with those carried by the ions of an electrolyte. In the molecule of HCl, for example, I picture the components of the hydrogen atoms as held together by a great number of tubes of electrostatic forces; the components of the chlorine atom are similarly held together, while only one stray tube bonds the hydrogen atom to the chlorine atom. The reason for attributing this high charge to the constituents of the atom is derived from the values of the specific inductive capacity of gases: we may imagine that the specific inductive capacity of a gas is due to the setting in the electric field of the electric doublet formed by the two oppositely electrified atoms which form the molecule of the gas. The measurements of the specific inductive capacity show, however, that this is very approximately an additive quantity: that is, that we can assign a certain value to each element, and find the specific inductive capacity of HCl by adding the value for hydrogen to the value for chlorine; the value of H_2O by adding twice the value for hydrogen to the value for oxygen, and so on. Now the electrical moment of the doublet formed by a positive charge on one atom of the molecule and a negative charge on the other atom would not be an additive property; if however, each atom had a definite electrical moment, and this were large compared with the electrical moment of the two atoms in the molecule, then the electrical moment of any compound and hence its specific inductive capacity, would be an additive property. For the electrical moment of the atom, however, to be large compared with that of the molecule, the charge on the corpuscles would have to be very large compared with those on the ion.

This conjecture of Thomson's was soon shown to be incorrect, largely as a result of experiments carried out in his own laboratory. Together with his student J. S. Townsend, Thomson initiated a series of experiments designed to measure the charge of the electron. A direct measurement of the electron's charge is very difficult to achieve; what Thomson and Townsend actually measured was the charge carried by gaseous ions, by a method which was the forerunner of Millikan's oil drop experiment, described in Chapter 1. The method was based on the important observation, made by Wilson in 1897, that water droplets tend to condense around charged particles. From the motion of these droplets under gravity and in electric fields, their charges could be calculated. The charges on the droplets turned out to be, within the rather large experimental error, integral multiples of the Stoney electron determined from electrochemistry.

In order to deduce from these results that the electron's charge is equal to the Stoney electron it was necessary to assume that the ions were formed from neutral gas molecules by the addition (or removal) of one or more electrons. This mechanism seems plausible and is indeed correct, but it could not have been considered obvious at the time. The most convincing experiments were those in which negative ions were obtained by shining ultraviolet light on a metal surface in contact with the gas. Since photoelectrons were known to be emitted, it seemed fairly clear that the ions were formed by the attachment of these photoelectrons on gas atoms. Nonetheless, a truly direct measurement of the electron's charge or mass was not achieved until many years later.

4. Canal rays and mass spectrometry. Another interesting phenomenon of the gas discharge was first observed by E. Goldstein in 1886: yellow rays which moved toward the cathode from the direction of the anode. When small holes were bored in the cathode, the rays could be seen streaming through to the opposite side. Goldstein [7] called these beams *Kanalstrahlen* (canal rays).

Since the canal rays traveled in the opposite direction from the cathode rays, it seemed reasonable to assume that they consist of positively charged particles. However, if this were true, the canal rays should have been deflectable by electric and magnetic fields, just as cathode rays are. Goldstein tried to achieve such a deflection but without success. (Because the canal rays are ions with a much lower specific charge than electrons, their deflections in a given field are correspondingly smaller.) A successful observation of the electric and magnetic deflections was not carried out until 12 years later, by W. Wien [8].

In Wien's experiment, a collimated beam of canal rays was made to pass through a region which contained strong parallel electric and magnetic fields, perpendicular to the beam direction. The arrangement is

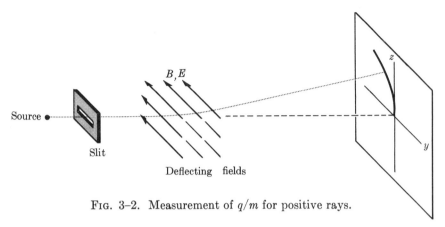

FIG. 3-2. Measurement of q/m for positive rays.

shown schematically in Fig. 3-2. If x denotes the direction of the beam and y that of the fields, then the electric deflection is in the y-direction and the magnetic deflection along z. (This remains approximately true as long as the deflections are small; see the discussion following Eq. (3-3).) The magnitudes of the deflections can be obtained from Eqs. (3-1) and (3-3). If an observation screen is located at a distance L from the deflecting region, a beam particle of velocity v and specific charge q/m strikes the screen at the point defined by the coordinates

$$y = \frac{qElL}{mv^2},$$
$$z = \frac{qBlL}{mvc},$$

(3-6)

where l is, as before, the length of the deflecting region. Eliminating v from these equations gives

$$z^2 = y\,\frac{B^2}{E}\,\frac{q}{m}\,\frac{lL}{c^2},$$

(3-7)

the equation of a parabola; all particles with a given specific charge should land somewhere on this parabola, no matter what their velocity. If the beam consists of particles with a single value of q/m, a single parabola should be observed. If more than one specific charge is present, a separate parabola should be observed for each.

Unfortunately, the pressure in Wien's apparatus was too high to allow the observation of discrete parabolas. Collisions with gas molecules deviated enough of the rays to smear out the traces, and Wien's observations indicated a continuous distribution of specific charges. This conclusion was, of course, incorrect. However, Wien was able to conclude correctly that the canal rays are positively charged particles and that their specific charge is roughly one-thousandth as large as that of electrons; that is, it is of the same order as the specific charge of ions in solution, which is obtained from electrochemical data.

Wien's technique was perfected by Thomson in a series of experiments beginning in 1906 [9]. Working at lower pressures, Thomson successfully observed discrete parabolas and thus demonstrated directly for the first time that atoms have discrete masses.

The specific charge of the canal rays, unlike that of cathode rays, was found to depend very closely on the composition of the gas in the discharge tube. The calculated values of q/m confirmed the hypothesis that the canal rays were, indeed, ions of the gases present in the tube. Thomson's parabolas mark the beginning of modern mass spectrometry. With the assumption that the charge is always a small multiple of e, the mass of the ion can be calculated.

The experiments with his mass spectrometer soon led Thomson to a new discovery. For some elements two or more parabolas could be resolved, indicating small differences in specific charge. Since these differences could not be due to multiple ionization, it followed that there must exist atoms of the same chemical element which have different masses, that is, isotopes.

The first element to be analyzed into more than one isotope in Thomson's laboratory was neon, in 1913. The average atomic weight for neon, as determined by gas chemistry, is approximately 20.2. The spectrometer resolved the neon spectrum into two parabolas, one corresponding to mass 20 and the other to mass 22. For some time Thomson was unconvinced that the mass-22 parabola might not have been caused by the hydride of normal neon, NeH_2. However, when the parabola persisted even after

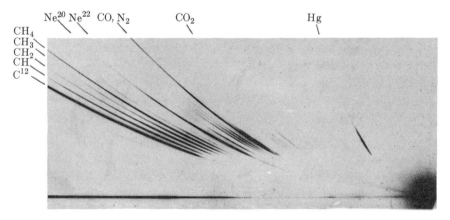

FIG. 3–3.   Parabolas obtained from a modern version of Thomson's mass spectrometer. (Photograph courtesy Prof. K. T. Bainbridge.)

repeated purification it became clear that the heavy isotope was present. This was the first demonstration of isotopy in stable elements, although the existence of isotopes for certain heavy elements had already been inferred by Soddy from the study of radioactive decay chains (see Section 3–7).

Figure 3–3 is typical of the results obtainable by means of Thomson's parabola method. (The actual data shown were taken by Bainbridge, considerably later.) It may be noted that the part of each parabola near the apex is absent. According to Eq. (3–6), small deflections correspond to ions of high velocity, which are the ones formed in the vicinity of the anode; the velocity of the most rapid ions is approximately given by

$$v_{\max}^2 = \frac{2qV_0}{m} \, , \qquad (3\text{--}8)$$

where V_0 is the anode potential. Equation (3–8), together with (3–6), implies that the y-deflection of the most rapid ion is

$$y_{\min} = \frac{ElL}{2V_0} \, . \qquad (3\text{--}9)$$

According to Eq. (3–9), all the parabolas should be cut off at the same minimum y, regardless of the value of q/m. As the figure shows, this prediction is essentially verified. (A couple of parabolas continue faintly to a value of $y_{\min}$ which is about half that of the others. Such traces must have been caused by doubly charged ions which lost one of their charges before passing through the deflecting plates.)

The accuracy achievable by Thomson's parabola method was limited chiefly by two factors. First, because the velocity spectrum of a single specific charge was spread out over a curve, the intensity reaching any one point was quite low. If a particular isotope were present only in minute amounts in the sample being analyzed, the trace it caused might have been so weak as to be unnoticeable. Secondly, the parabola method had no directional focusing properties. Two ions which happened to enter the deflecting region at a slightly divergent angle would have become further separated by the time they reached the plane of observation. This effect decreased both the accuracy of an individual mass measurement and the resolution of the apparatus.

Later developments in mass spectrometry were designed to concentrate at a single point as many ions as possible of a given specific charge, irrespective of their velocity or direction. Different arrangements emphasized either velocity or directional focusing. Figure 3–4 shows the simplest type of directional focusing. Ions pass through the slits S_1, S_2, and enter a region which contains a magnetic field B, normal to the plane of the paper. They then travel on circular paths with diameters given by

$$D = \frac{2mvc}{qB}. \qquad (3\text{-}10)$$

The figure shows the path of two representative ions; one of these enters the field region in a direction normal to the plane of the slit, the other at a small angle α to the normal. The linear separation of the two ions after they have traversed a semicircle is given by

$$\Delta = D(1 - \cos \alpha) \approx D\alpha^2/2. \qquad (3\text{-}11)$$

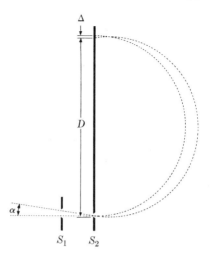

FIG. 3-4. 180° Magnetic focusing.

Since the separation is quadratic in the small quantity α, the rays may be said to be focused. This design does not, however, achieve any velocity focusing; therefore, care must be taken to ensure that the rays have very nearly the same velocity when they enter the region of magnetic field. A common procedure is to place a crossed-field velocity selector between the two slits.

Improvements in mass spectrographic technique were contributed by Aston, Dempster, Bainbridge, and many others [10]. Complicated geometrical arrangements were devised in order to achieve simultaneous velocity and directional focusing, and exceedingly high accuracy and resolution have been attained.

Some typical results of mass spectrographic analysis are presented in Table 3-1. It must be kept in mind that the scales used for atomic masses have undergone a number of changes. When oxygen was first adopted as the standard, it was assigned the exact mass 16. After the discovery of the rare isotopes O^{17} and O^{18} (they comprise about $\frac{1}{4}\%$ of normal oxygen), a physical scale was adopted in which the isotope O^{16} was assigned the value 16. The atomic mass unit (amu) was defined as $\frac{1}{16}$ the mass of O^{16}. In the chemical scale the average mass of oxygen had the defining role; the two scales differed by 0.0278%. In an effort to reconcile the difference, an international commission in 1961 decided to change the physical mass scale and assign to the isotope C^{12} the exact mass 12.0. This change reduced all mass values by about 0.032%; the new physical scale differs from the chemical scale by only 43 parts per million.

The data in the table are given in the new C^{12} scale. Whichever scale is used, however, one crude fact stands out: the masses of the isotopes

TABLE 3–1

MASS AND NATURAL ABUNDANCE OF STABLE ISOTOPES

For Z > 13, only the most abundant isotope of each element is listed. Masses are referred to the standard $C^{12} \equiv 12$. Masses taken from Everling, et al. [11].

Z	Symbol	A	Abundance %	Mass
1	H	1	99.985	1.0078252
		2	0.015	2.0141022
2	He	3	0.00013	3.0160299
		4	100	4.0026036
3	Li	6	7.52	6.0151263
		7	92.48	7.0160053
4	Be	9	100	9.0121858
5	B	10	18.98	10.0129389
		11	81.02	11.0093051
6	C	12	98.89	12.0000000
		13	1.11	13.0033543
7	N	14	99.64	14.0030744
		15	0.36	15.0001081
8	O	16	99.76	15.9949149
		17	0.037	16.9991334
		18	0.204	17.9991598
9	F	19	100	18.9984046
10	Ne	20	90.8	19.9924404
		21	0.26	20.993849
		22	8.9	21.9913845
11	Na	23	100	22.989773
12	Mg	24	78.60	23.985045
		25	10.11	24.985540
		26	11.29	25.982591
13	Al	27	100	26.981535
14	Si	28	92.27	27.976927
15	P	31	100	30.973763
16	S	32	95.06	31.972074
17	Cl	35	75.4	34.968855
18	Ar	40	99.60	39.9623838
19	K	39	93.08	38.963714
20	Ca	40	96.97	39.962589
21	Sc	45	100	44.955919
22	Ti	48	73.45	47.947948
23	V	51	99.76	50.943978
24	Cr	52	83.76	51.940514
25	Mn	55	100	54.938054
26	Fe	56	91.68	55.934932
27	Co	59	100	58.933189
28	Ni	58	67.76	57.935342
29	Cu	63	69.1	62.929594
30	Zn	64	48.89	63.929145
31	Ga	69	60.2	68.925682
32	Ge	74	36.74	73.921150
33	As	75	100	74.921580
34	Se	80	49.82	79.916512
35	Br	79	55.2	78.918348
36	Kr	84	57.0	83.911504
37	Rb	85	72.15	84.91171
38	Sr	88	82.56	87.90561
39	Y	89	100	88.90632
40	Zr	90	51.46	89.90432
41	Nb	93	100	92.90602
42	Mo	98	23.75	97.90551
44	Ru	102	31.70	101.90372
45	Rh	103	100	102.90480
46	Pd	106	27.33	105.90320
47	Ag	107	51.35	106.90497
48	Cd	114	28.86	113.90357
49	In	115	95.77	114.90407
50	Sn	120	32.97	119.90213
51	Sb	121	57.25	120.90375
52	Te	128	31.79	127.90471
53	I	127	100	126.90435
54	Xe	132	26.9	131.90416
55	Cs	133	100	132.90509
56	Ba	138	71.66	137.90501
57	La	139	99.9	138.90606
(Rare earths omitted)				
72	Hf	180	35.44	179.94512
73	Ta	181	99.988	180.94618
74	W	184	30.6	183.94915
75	Re	187	62.93	186.95498
76	Os	192	41.0	191.96051
77	Ir	193	62.7	192.96234
78	Pt	195	33.7	194.96446
79	Au	197	100	196.96655
80	Hg	202	29.8	201.97063
81	Tl	205	70.50	204.97446
82	Pb	208	52.3	207.97664

are rather well represented as multiples of a single unit, which is approximately the mass of a hydrogen atom.

In 1815 Prout had suggested that all matter might be constructed of a single building block, the hydrogen atom. This hypothesis requires that the mass of every atom be an integral multiple of the hydrogen mass. With the development of gas-chemical and electrochemical measurements of atomic masses in the following years, Prout's hypothesis apparently became untenable. It could not account for such values of atomic mass as 35.5 for chlorine or 20.2 for neon. After the discovery of isotopes, when it was realized that the chemical atomic masses are only average values, and the individual isotopic masses are nearly integral multiples of the same unit, Prout's hypothesis once again became plausible. However, two difficulties remained. First, the unit in terms of which the masses were close to integers was not exactly the hydrogen mass, but about 1% smaller. Secondly, even in terms of this unit, there remained small deviations from integral masses.

A resolution of both difficulties is supplied by the special theory of relativity. If the Prout hypothesis is correct, and an atom of mass number A consists of A hydrogen atoms, these must be held together by some attractive force, that is, with a negative potential energy (positive binding energy). According to relativity, the binding energy is equivalent to a "mass defect": the atomic mass is less than the total mass of the constituents by $1/c^2$ times the binding energy:

$$M_A = A m_\mathrm{H} - \frac{\Delta}{c^2}, \qquad (3\text{--}12)$$

where Δ is the energy required to disassociate the atom in question into A hydrogen atoms. If the measured masses were exact multiples of a single unit, $M_A = A\mathfrak{M}$, they would be consistent with Prout's hypothesis and the rule that the binding energy of an atom is proportional to A:

$$\Delta = A(m_\mathrm{H} - \mathfrak{M})c^2. \qquad (3\text{--}13)$$

The actual masses therefore require only slight deviations from the rule (3–13), if $\mathfrak{M}$ has a value about 0.99 m_H. The present-day interpretation of atomic masses is still based on Eq. (3–12), modified only to take into account the presence of more than one "building block."* Taken in a broad sense, Prout's hypothesis has therefore proved to be correct.

5. Early views on atomic composition. The discussion of mass spectrometry has taken us considerably ahead of historical sequence in the

---

* The actual calculation of binding energies from an assumed force law is of course a far more complicated matter.

understanding of atomic composition. At first, only the presence of
electrons was an established fact. It was clear that atoms must also contain positive charge, but the early data shed little light on its identity.
The nature of the positive component became a subject of intense speculation at the beginning of the new century. It seemed reasonable to some
(for example, to Larmor and Lorentz) that a positively charged particle,
otherwise identical to the electron, should exist and play a symmetric
role in the atom; however, no evidence for the existence of such a particle
appeared.*

The state of confusion is best described by a quotation from a book
published by Lodge in 1906 [12]. Discussing the constitution of hydrogen,
he lists the following possibilities:

(1) The main bulk of the atom may consist of ordinary matter (whatever
unknown entity is hidden by that familiar phrase), associated with sufficient
positive electricity (whatever that may be) to neutralise the charge belonging
to the electron or electrons which undoubtedly exist in connection with
each atom.

(2) Or the bulk of the atom may consist of a multitude of positive and negative
electrons, interleaved, as it were, and holding themselves together in a cluster
by their mutual attractions, whether in a state of intricate orbital motion, or
in some static geometrical configuration, kept permanent by appropriate
connexions.

(3) Or the bulk of the atom may be composed of an indivisible unit of positive
electricity, constituting a presumably spherical mass or "jelly," in the midst
of which an electrically equivalent number of point electrons are, as it were,
'sown'; . . .†

(4) It may consist of a kind of interlocked admixture of positive and negative
electricity, indivisible and inseparable into units, and incapable of being
appreciably sheared by applied forces, but incorporated together as a continuous mass; in the midst of which one or more isolated and individualised
electrons may move about and carry on that display of external activity
which confers upon the atom its observed properties.

(5) A fifth view of the atom would regard it as a central 'sun' of extremely
concentrated positive electricity at the centre, with a multitude of electrons
revolving in astronomical orbits, like asteroids, within its range of attraction.‡ But this would give a law of inverse square for the force, and
consequently periodic times dependent on distance, which appears not to
correspond with anything satisfactorily observed.

Much of the confusion was due to the fact that, for quite some time,
there was essentially no evidence concerning the *number* of electrons present

---

* The positive electron was discovered in 1932, by C. D. Anderson. Being
an antiparticle, it plays no part in ordinary atomic structure.

† This is Thomson's atom, discussed in detail in the next section.

‡ The nuclear atom, see Sections 10 and 12.

within any atom. It was at first believed that this number must be very large; if matter were composed entirely of positive and negative electrons, for example, there would have to be almost 2000 in a hydrogen atom. Such a situation would help resolve some of the difficulties connected with radiative stability (Section 6, p. 73).

It is not hard to think of objections to the all-electron hypothesis. Why, for example, if atoms contain many thousands of particles, do so few distinct elements exist? And why was no positive ion ever observed with a specific charge higher than that of the hydrogen ion? Without benefit of hindsight, however, arguments of this sort seem much less compelling.

In 1906 Thomson published an important paper [13] which presented three different arguments to indicate that the number of electrons in an atom is actually quite small, of the order of the mass number.* Two of the arguments were based on the scattering of x-rays and the dispersion of light in gases (both of which are discussed in Volume 2); the third made use of preliminary data on the absorption of cathode rays and β-rays in matter (Section 3–9). These data were none too accurate, and the theories on which the arguments were based have all undergone substantial modifications. It is therefore not surprising that some of the estimates of electron numbers proved to be considerably in error. Nevertheless, the orders of magnitude were sufficient to definitely exclude the all-electron atom, as well as several other possible models. All subsequent data confirmed Thomson's qualitative conclusion that the electron numbers are small, although their exact values were not determined until considerably later.†

The knowledge that electron numbers are small allowed an indirect conclusion to be drawn concerning the remaining components of the atom: they must carry almost all the mass. Nothing else was known about the positive component until Rutherford demonstrated the existence of the nucleus in 1911. Ideas on the composition of the nucleus were stimulated by the mass-spectroscopic data described in the preceding section; these data became available in quantity only after 1915. The emergence of the proton as a fundamental atomic constituent is discussed in Section 3–11.

6. The Thomson atom. Until 1911 the most popular model of the atom was the one proposed by Thomson in 1904 [15–17]. Thomson postulated that the positively charged component is distributed uniformly throughout a sphere which defines the atomic volume. The positive "fluid" was

---

* According to Lodge [ref. 12, p. 151], this was "an extraordinary and unexpected result." Lodge's subsequent remarks make interesting reading as a contemporary view.

† As late as 1911, H. A. Wilson "concluded," from a theoretical argument based on the Thomson model, that a hydrogen atom contains eight electrons [14].

assumed to act on negative charges through electrical forces only, although some additional mechanism had to be invoked to hold the fluid itself together. The nature of this mechanism was not specified in the theory; it might be considered as roughly analogous to the force of cohesion in liquids. The radius of the atom was taken, on the basis of kinetic theory and other considerations, to be of the order of 10^{-8} cm. (The model itself carries no intrinsic unit of size.)

The electrons, in Thomson's model, are point charges distributed throughout the positive fluid, either at rest or rotating about the center in circular orbits. They are subject to their mutual repulsion as well as to the central field of the positive fluid, which varies linearly with radius. For small numbers of electrons, the equilibrium configurations are easy to deduce. A single electron resides at the center of the atom. Two electrons assume symmetrical positions on opposite sides of the center, one radius apart if they are at rest. If they rotate, their separation must be greater; the equilibrium radius b of the orbit is found to be

$$b = \frac{a}{2}\left(1 - \frac{m\omega^2 a^3}{2e^2}\right)^{-1/3}, \qquad (3\text{--}14)$$

where a is the radius of the positive fluid and ω the rotation frequency. The latter can take any value between zero and some maximum, which makes $b = a$. Any faster rotation would put the electrons outside the fluid; equilibrium is still possible but the orbit radius is no longer given by (3–14). Such orbits were not considered by Thomson.

Three electrons form an equilateral triangle, which likewise can either remain static or rotate in its own plane. The equilibrium radius is

$$b = \frac{a}{\sqrt{3}}\left(1 - \frac{m\omega^2 a^3}{3e^2}\right)^{-1/3}. \qquad (3\text{--}15)$$

In the static case, the side of the triangle, $b\sqrt{3}$, is just equal to the radius of the sphere (Fig. 3–5).

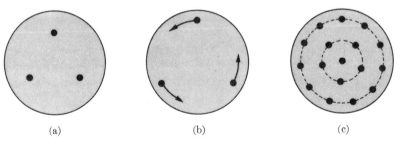

(a)   (b)   (c)

Fig. 3–5. The Thomson model. (a) Static three-electron atom. (b) Dynamic three-electron atom. (c) 17-electron atom. The shading indicates the positive fluid.

With four electrons, three distinct equilibrium configurations are possible. The electrons may be found at the corners of a regular tetrahedron or of a square; or three of them may form a triangle, with the fourth at the center. Each of these configurations may either remain static or rotate. However, Thomson found that the square array is not stable against perturbations normal to its own plane unless it rotates at a frequency faster than some critical value. For larger electron numbers, the possible equilibrium configurations rapidly proliferate. Many of the possibilities can be excluded on the basis of stability considerations; for example, eight electrons at the corners of a cube are unstable no matter how rapidly they rotate.

The general problem of finding all possible equilibrium arrangements of n electrons is extremely complicated, and Thomson did not succeed in solving it. He did, however, analyze quite thoroughly the special case in which the electrons are confined to a single plane through the center of the atom. This analysis led to several interesting results. In the first place, it is clear that a solution always exists in the form of a ring, with the electrons evenly spaced around it. However, when $n > 5$ such a ring turns out to be always unstable. For $n = 6, 7, 8$, or 9, a ring with one electron at the center is stable. With 10 electrons, at least two must go in the interior in order to give stability. These two do not, of course, stay at the center but form their own "inner ring."

Thomson was able to show that a ring of m electrons cannot be stable unless it contains at least p others inside it. The value of p increases rapidly with m, as shown in Table 3–2. When m is large, p is proportional to m^3. If the inner ring consists of six or more electrons, it must itself enclose some interior electrons in order to be stable. Evidently, as the total number of electrons increases, the number of rings must also increase.

The stability condition summarized in Table 3–2 is not sufficient to determine a unique ring structure for a given number of electrons. For example, with $n = 13$ the configurations $(10, 3)$, $(9, 4)$, $(8, 5)$, as well as

TABLE 3–2

MINIMUM NUMBER OF INTERIOR ELECTRONS (p) REQUIRED TO
MAKE A RING OF m ELECTRONS STABLE

m	2–5	6–8	9	10	11	12	13	14	15	16
p	0	1	2	3	5	8	10	14	15	19

m	17	18	19	20	21	22	23	24	30	40
p	25	32	36	39	47	56	63	69	101	232

TABLE 3–3 RING STRUCTURE OF ATOMS ACCORDING TO THOMSON MODEL

[The symbol $(a, b, c, \ldots)$ denotes the population of successive rings, starting from the outside.]

Electron number n

1–5	6–16	17–31	32–48	49–69	70–93	94–
(1)	(5, 1)	(11, 5, 1)	(15, 11, 5, 1)	(17, 15, 11, 5, 1)	(21, 17, 15, 11, 5, 1)	(24, 21, 17, 15, 11, 5, 1)
(2)	(6, 1)	(11, 6, 1)	(15, 11, 6, 1)	(18, 15, 11, 5, 1)	(21, 18, 15, 11, 5, 1)	(24, 21, 18, 15, 11, 5, 1)
(3)	(7, 1)	(11, 7, 1)	(15, 11, 7, 1)	(18, 15, 11, 6, 1)	(21, 18, 15, 11, 6, 1)	(24, 21, 18, 15, 11, 6, 1)
(4)	(8, 1)	(12, 7, 1)	(16, 11, 7, 1)	(18, 15, 11, 7, 1)	(21, 18, 15, 11, 7, 1)	(24, 21, 18, 15, 11, 7, 1)
(5)	(8, 2)	(12, 8, 1)	(16, 12, 7, 1)	(18, 16, 11, 7, 1)	(21, 18, 16, 11, 7, 1)	(24, 21, 18, 16, 11, 7, 1)
	(9, 2)	(12, 8, 2)	(16, 12, 8, 1)	(18, 16, 12, 7, 1)	(21, 18, 16, 12, 7, 1)	(24, 21, 18, 16, 12, 7, 1)
	(9, 3)	(13, 8, 2)	(16, 12, 8, 2)	(19, 16, 12, 7, 1)	(21, 19, 16, 12, 7, 1)	(24, 21, 19, 16, 12, 7, 1)
	(10, 3)	(13, 9, 2)	(16, 13, 8, 2)	(19, 16, 12, 8, 1)	(21, 19, 16, 12, 8, 1)	
	(10, 4)	(13, 9, 3)	(16, 13, 9, 2)	(19, 16, 12, 8, 2)	(22, 19, 16, 12, 8, 1)	
	(10, 5)	(13, 10, 3)	(16, 13, 9, 3)	(19, 16, 13, 8, 2)	(22, 19, 16, 12, 8, 2)	
	(11, 5)	(13, 10, 4)	(17, 13, 10, 3)	(20, 16, 13, 8, 2)	(22, 19, 16, 13, 8, 2)	
		(14, 10, 4)	(17, 13, 10, 4)	(20, 16, 13, 9, 2)	(22, 19, 16, 13, 8, 2)	
		(14, 10, 5)	(17, 14, 10, 4)	(20, 16, 13, 9, 3)	(22, 20, 16, 13, 8, 2)	
		(15, 10, 5)	(17, 15, 10, 5)	(20, 17, 13, 9, 3)	(22, 20, 16, 13, 9, 2)	
		(15, 11, 5)	(17, 15, 11, 5)	(20, 17, 13, 10, 3)	(22, 20, 16, 13, 9, 3)	
				(20, 17, 13, 10, 4)	(22, 20, 17, 13, 9, 3)	
				(20, 17, 14, 10, 4)	(22, 20, 17, 13, 10, 3)	
				(20, 17, 14, 10, 5)	(23, 20, 17, 13, 10, 3)	
				(20, 17, 15, 10, 5)	(23, 20, 17, 13, 10, 4)	
				(21, 17, 15, 10, 5)	(23, 20, 17, 14, 10, 4)	
				(21, 17, 15, 11, 5)	(23, 20, 17, 14, 10, 5)	
					(23, 20, 17, 15, 10, 5)	
					(23, 21, 17, 15, 10, 5)	
					(23, 21, 17, 15, 11, 5)	
					(24, 21, 17, 15, 11, 5)	

many others, are all stable. [The symbol $(a, b, c \ldots)$ denotes the populations of successive rings, starting from the outside.] Thomson chose among the alternatives by stipulating that each ring should enclose the *minimum* number of interior electrons consistent with the stability requirement. That is, as many electrons as possible should go on the outside.* The configurations determined by this criterion are listed in Table 3–3 up to $n = 100$, which requires seven rings.

Thomson's ideas on ring structure were partly stimulated by experiments carried out by Mayer, using magnetized needles inserted in corks which floated in water. All the north poles pointed up; when the needles were fairly close together, they repelled each other with approximately an inverse-square force (neglecting the effect of the distant south poles). A large magnet was placed above the surface of the water, with its south pole down. The field of this magnet is such that its component along the surface of the water is directed toward the point vertically below the magnet and is approximately proportional to the distance from this point. The system therefore forms an analogue to the planar Thomson model, the needles playing the role of the electrons and the large magnet the role of the positive fluid. When Mayer put various numbers of needles under the magnet they arranged themselves, with a few exceptions, into rings with precisely the configurations given in Table 3–3. This agreement justified Thomson's criterion for choosing among competing configurations.

Thomson did not suggest that electrons in real atoms actually assume the planar arrays which he had derived. However, he argued that the more probable three-dimensional arrangements ought to show similar characteristics. Instead of forming rings, the electrons presumably form spherical shells, with each shell required to enclose a minimum number of electrons in order to be stable. Of course the populations of the shells need bear no particular relation to the numbers calculated for the rings; however, the qualitative properties of the ring structures led to some appealing speculations. The most noticeable feature of Table 3–3 is that all the configurations in each column consistently recur in the next column, surrounded by an additional ring. It is not unreasonable to expect that chemical properties should be associated with particular groupings of electrons; the theory therefore suggests that a systematic repetition of chemical properties should take place among groups of elements. For

---

* It is not obvious that this criterion picks out the minimum-energy configuration, which would presumably constitute the normal state of the atom if the model were correct. The energy balance between the electrons' mutual repulsion and their interaction with the positive fluid is a delicate one, and without a detailed calculation it is impossible to tell which of two configurations has a lower energy. In simple cases, it may be verified that Thomson's criterion does minimize the energy (see Problem 3–1).

example, the elements with configurations (8, 2), (12, 8, 2), (16, 12, 8, 2), and so on, should all be chemically similar. This interpretation of the periodic table on the basis of shell structure was probably the most lasting feature of Thomson's atomic model. Its only essential difference from the present-day view is that Thomson's argument associates chemical behavior with the structure of interior shells rather than with the outermost one.*

Thomson's theory also offered an explanation for the successive changes in chemical valence from one atom to the next in the same row of the periodic table. The reasoning was based on the fact that, in the Thomson model, many successive atoms have the same number of electrons in their outermost shell. Inasmuch as this property is not retained in the modern view of the atom, the argument has little relevance to current ideas on valence and will not be presented here.

When the equilibrium arrangement of a Thomson atom is disturbed slightly, the electrons respond as a system of coupled oscillators. Their motion is a superposition of sinusoidal oscillations (normal modes); the natural or resonant frequencies associated with these normal modes determine most of the electromagnetic properties of the atom.† The frequencies appear as parameters in Lorentz's electron theory (described in the following volume), which furnishes a qualitatively satisfactory explanation for optical dispersion, the scattering of radiation, and similar phenomena. On the other hand, according to classical electromagnetic theory the natural frequencies should also coincide with the radiation emitted and absorbed by atoms. The spectra which Thomson calculated for atoms with relatively small electron numbers were indeed in the optical region or nearby; however, they did not agree with the lines actually measured for any element. This result in itself was not of great import; since the frequencies were calculated from the two-dimensional ring model, they could hardly have been expected to be quantitatively correct. But the failure to predict anything resembling the recently identified spectral series had to be considered a definite shortcoming of the model.

The number of lines in the observed emission and absorption spectra presented another serious problem. In classical theory each electron contributes three oscillators, one for each degree of freedom; the number of frequencies is therefore only three times the electron number (and even smaller if there is degeneracy). If the number of electrons is small, classical

---

* Thomson made no attempt to deduce the structure of specific elements; such a program would have required at the very least a knowledge of the three-dimensional solutions. Therefore there could be no detailed comparison with the actual periodic table.

† The requirement that these frequencies be real leads to the stability condition which underlies the entire model.

TABLE 3-4

ATTENUATION OF RADIATION FOR RINGS
OF CIRCULATING ELECTRONS (AFTER THOMSON)

No. of electrons in ring	Radiation from each electron	
	$v = 0.1c$	$v = 0.01c$
1	1	1
2	9.6×10^{-2}	9.6×10^{-4}
3	4.6×10^{-3}	4.6×10^{-7}
4	1.7×10^{-4}	1.7×10^{-10}
5	5.6×10^{-5}	5.6×10^{-13}
6	1.6×10^{-7}	1.6×10^{-17}

theory predicts far too few lines. The spectroscopic observation of large numbers of lines for each element was in fact one of the major reasons for the early belief that the electron numbers had to be large.

In the rotating version of Thomson's "plum-pudding" model, one final problem had to be considered. According to classical electromagnetic theory the electrons, being accelerated, should radiate energy continuously even when they are in their normal state; the atom is therefore unstable. This difficulty was never satisfactorily resolved. Thomson pointed out, however, that when several electrons equally spaced on a ring rotate together, destructive interference cuts down the radiation by a very large factor, especially at low velocity. (When a uniform charge distribution rotates, there is no radiation at all.) Table 3-4 gives the attenuation factor for $v = 0.1c$ and $0.01c$. The rate of radiation decreases rapidly with the number of electrons in a ring. If all atoms contained very many electrons, as was originally believed, the amount of radiation from the normal state might be so small as to be unobservable. There would then be no contradiction between a dynamical model and the "apparent" stability of atoms.* This argument collapsed, of course, as soon as the correct electron numbers were ascertained.

The fact that rotating rings radiate slowly was actually utilized by Thomson in an ingenious (although incorrect) explanation for the phenomenon of radioactivity. His argument was based on the result that

---

* Furthermore, it can be argued that matter at ordinary temperatures does radiate weakly and is maintained in equilibrium by continual emission and absorption. The entire subject of radiation is treated in much greater detail in the next volume.

certain configurations are stable only when the rotation frequency exceeds some critical value. If an atom originally found itself in such a configuration it would gradually slow down as energy was radiated, until the critical frequency was reached. At this point the motion would suddenly become unstable and a violent rearrangement would take place inside the atom. Such a rearrangement would release considerable energy, which might be sufficient to expel one or more particles from the atom. The process bears a close resemblance to the behavior of tops, for which certain motions are also stable only when the rotation speed exceeds a critical value. As the top slows down because of frictional losses, it eventually reaches the critical frequency, and a drastic change in the motion suddenly takes place; for example, the top may flip over.

7. The identification of α- and β-rays. The evidence which brought about the demise of the Thomson atom was supplied largely by scattering experiments which succeeded in probing the atomic interior. It was fortunate that, at just the opportune time, probes were discovered which could penetrate the atom and furnish such evidence. In 1895 Henri Becquerel found, by accident, that uranium salts emit radiation which can pass through matter and affect a photographic plate.

The discovery of radioactive elements is a familiar story; for present purposes it is the radiations themselves that are the subject of interest. These radiations exhibited several novel properties. Becquerel showed that they not only would darken photographic plates but would also discharge electrified bodies and ionize the molecules of air or other gases through which they passed. All of these properties could be used to detect the presence of the radiations. Another method of detection was based on Wilson's observation, already mentioned in Section 3, that water vapor tends to condense around ions; under the proper conditions the tracks of the rays of radioactivity could be made visible by such condensation of water droplets. This is the principle of the cloud chamber, a tool extensively used up to the present day.

Using such ionization techniques, early investigators of radioactivity were able to separate the radiations into three types, which they designated as α, β, and γ. The three types were distinguished by their ability to penetrate matter, by the amount of ionization they produce, and by their deflectability in electric or magnetic fields. Alpha rays are heavily ionizing; they make many ion pairs per centimeter of track in gas. They are not, as a rule, able to penetrate any great thickness of matter. Magnetic deflection experiments showed that α-rays are positively charged and that all the rays from a given source have very nearly the same velocity or, at most, a few discrete velocities. Beta rays are usually more penetrating than α-rays and ionize less heavily along their paths; in magnetic fields they are deflected as a negative charge stream with a continuous velocity spectrum. The continuous nature of the β-ray spectrum was established relatively late (1914) by Chadwick, but the wide range of β-ray velocities was known very early. Gamma rays, the third type of radiation, are the most difficult to detect. They cause very little ionization, are undeflected by magnetic or electric fields, and are able to penetrate great thicknesses of matter.

The use of the newly discovered radiations as probes of the atom required a knowledge of their precise nature. The identification of β-rays as electrons and α-rays as helium ions was therefore of paramount importance in the understanding of atomic structure.

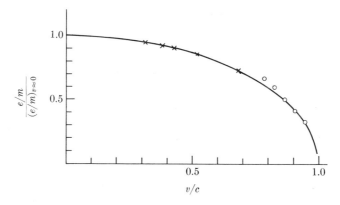

FIG. 3–6. Specific charge of β-rays as a function of velocity, normalized to 1 at zero velocity. The circles are the data of Kaufmann [18], the crosses of Bucherer [19]. The solid curve is the variation predicted by relativity.

Not long after β-rays were discovered, they were shown to be identical with electrons. Becquerel measured the specific charge in 1899, and found that it was approximately the same as that of cathode rays. A more accurate measurement was achieved in 1901 by Kaufmann [18]. Kaufmann's data were the first to exhibit the decrease of specific charge with velocity, which was soon to be explained on the basis of the special theory of relativity. Figure 3–6 shows these measurements, together with some later ones by Bucherer [19]. The data are consistent with the variation of mass

$$m = \frac{m_0}{\sqrt{1 - (v/c)^2}}, \tag{3–16}$$

as predicted by special relativity. When the fast rays were slowed down by passage through matter, they again exhibited the specific charge characteristic of cathode rays. There was consequently no reason to doubt that all the β-rays were electrons. Recently Goldhaber and Scharff-

Goldhaber have performed an experiment [20] which demonstrated quite convincingly the identity of β-rays and electrons. The argument requires the use of quantum mechanics.*

That α-particles might be helium was suspected early because of the frequent occurrence of helium in association with the natural radioactive elements. Helium was found in conjunction with radium and uranium by Rutherford, Soddy, and Ramsay during the period 1902–1904. This observation suggested the possibility of collecting α-particles and attempting chemical identification of the neutralized rays. Standard chemical methods were not sensitive enough to accomplish such an identification, but spectroscopy provided a technique of sufficient sensitivity. Alpha particles were allowed to enter an evacuated discharge tube, and the spectrum of the discharge was examined; helium was found in the spectrum by Rutherford and Royds in 1909 [21]. This result strongly suggested that α-rays are helium ions, but it was somewhat indirect. Standard deflection experiments were also undertaken in an attempt to measure the specific charge of α-rays directly. Early measurements by Rutherford and by Des Coudres in 1903 gave a value about 1.8×10^{14} esu/gm. In 1914 Rutherford and Robinson [22] carefully determined the specific charge by measuring electric and magnetic deflections. Using the α-particles emitted by radium C, they obtained the value 1.45×10^{14} esu/gm, almost exactly half the specific charge of a normal hydrogen ion.

These experiments demonstrated only that an alpha particle must be either a singly charged hydrogen ion of double the normal mass (i.e., singly ionized deuterium), a doubly ionized helium atom, a triply ionized atom of Li^6, or something in the same sequence. In order to decide among the possibilities, it was necessary to measure the charge carried by the α-particle. Rutherford and Geiger [23] accomplished this by collecting the charge given off by a radioactive sample and counting the number of α-particles emitted in the same length of time. One of the major problems in the experiment was to make sure that the charge measured was indeed carried by the α-particles, and was not brought in either by β-radiation from the same source or as a result of ionization of the gas near the collecting electrode. Sizable errors due to these causes were avoided by employing the apparatus shown in Fig. 3–7. A source of radium C was deposited on a glass vessel and the emitted α-particles passed through a thin aluminum foil before falling on the plate. The foil served to prevent recoil atoms from arriving at the collector. The angle from which particles could arrive at the collector was defined by a diaphragm in front of the plate.

---

* The experiment showed that a beta ray and an atomic electron obey the Pauli exclusion principle, i.e., they cannot occupy the same quantum mechanical state. The Pauli principle applies only to identical particles.

The contribution of β-rays was eliminated by a strong magnetic field perpendicular to the direction of the stream of particles. The magnetic field deflected away the β-particles coming from the source and also served to return to the collector any electrons which were liberated from it by the impact of the α-particles. If these secondary electrons (sometimes called δ-rays) had not been returned, the effective charge measured at the collector would have been greater than the positive charge which actually arrived there.

If the number of particles emitted by the source per unit time is known, the determination of the number arriving at the collector becomes a problem of geometry. The entire method centers then on counting the actual number of α-rays emitted from a source. The fact that charged particles ionize the gases through which they travel makes possible the construction of electrical devices which can indicate the presence of a single α-ray. Under standard conditions in air each α-particle from radium C produces approximately 2.2×10^5 ion pairs. This

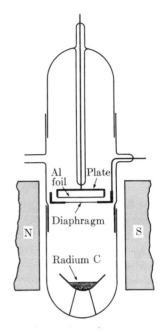

FIG. 3-7. Apparatus used by Rutherford and Geiger to measure the charge of the α-particle.

ionization is sufficient to be detectable if all the charge of one sign is communicated to an appropriate electrometer circuit.

In 1908 Rutherford and Geiger devised a more subtle method of counting [23]. They sent α-particles through a tube which contained gas at low pressure, in an electric field almost strong enough to cause breakdown. Under such conditions the ionization caused by the passage of a single charged particle is sufficient to initiate a far larger ionization in the gas, by an avalanche process. The ions originally created by the incident particle are accelerated by the field; they collide with gas atoms and produce additional ions which are themselves accelerated, and so on. A substantial current is quickly attained. This electrical pulse can be used to register a count; the apparatus therefore directly counts individual particles. Of course, before a second particle can be counted, all of the ions formed by the first must be collected and the initial conditions restored. During the time required to accomplish this resetting, the counter is insensitive or "dead." In the original apparatus only a few particles per minute could be counted. However, by 1912 technical improvements had reduced the dead-time appreciably, and counting rates as high as a thousand α-particles per minute were accurately recorded. The original counters were not so effective in detecting beta particles because of the smaller ionization produced by the betas. However, in the following year, Geiger developed a counter which was sensitive enough to detect beta rays.

The results of the counting experiments showed that a gram of radium emits 3.57×10^{10} α-particles per second. Once the emission rate was determined, the charge collection experiment could be combined with it to establish the charge carried by the individual α-particles. Rutherford and Geiger obtained the result $q_\alpha = 9.3 \times 10^{-10}$ esu. Similar experiments by Regner in 1909, using polonium as the source of α-particles, gave a value 9.57×10^{-10} esu, almost exactly twice the best modern value of the electronic charge. From this evidence together with the specific charge, it could be unambiguously concluded that α-particles are doubly charged helium atoms.

The experiments of Rutherford and Geiger were important, not only because of their incisive identification of the nature of the α-particle, but also because they marked the first time that individual atomic events were counted by electrical means. The use of counters to detect the passage of submicroscopic particles has become one of the most powerful techniques of modern experimental physics. Its elegance in showing the discrete nature of matter is surpassed only by the pictures of particle tracks supplied by cloud chambers, bubble chambers, and similar devices.

The gamma radiation was the most difficult of the three types to identify. Its most distinguishing property was the lack of deflection by electric or magnetic fields. It was early suspected that gamma rays are a form of electromagnetic radiation. The work of Gray (1917) and Rutherford and Andrade (1914) showed that γ-rays resemble x-rays. Gamma rays were of minor importance in the development of atomic physics; they became a useful tool only much later, in the study of nuclear structure.

The identification of α-rays and β-rays made it easy to understand the radioactive displacement law, which had been established from studies of the chemistry of the radioactive elements. Chemical separations of decay products had been carried out early in the history of radioactivity in an effort to discover the nature of the decay process. Three long chains, or radioactive series, were quickly established and a fourth has been discovered more recently.

Each radioactive decay results in a change in the chemical properties of the substance involved, and all the chains end in stable atoms of lead or bismuth. Very early in the chemical investigation it was found by McCoy and Ross that radiothorium and thorium, which belonged to different series, were not separable chemically. Likewise, Soddy and

Marckwald showed that radium and mesothorium were chemically identical. Soddy gave the name "isotope" to those atoms which appeared to belong to the same chemical element, but differed in their radioactive properties. It was at that time unknown in what other ways these isotopes of the same elements differ, since their masses had not yet been established. The displacement law was proposed on the basis of purely chemical evidence at essentially the same time by Russell, Soddy, and Fajans [24]. The law states that α-particle emission causes a shift of two places in the periodic table in the direction of the lighter elements, while β-emission causes a shift of one place in the direction of heavy elements. After the identification of the α- and β-rays, the origin of the law was of course apparent.

Among the chains of radioactive elements there are half a dozen examples of the sequence which consists of an alpha emission followed by two β-emissions. According to the displacement law, the original and final elements must then be chemically the same, but must differ isotopically by the mass of one α-particle. In each such case, therefore, it follows that here are isotopes which differ not only in their radioactive properties but also in their mass. A typical example is the sequence

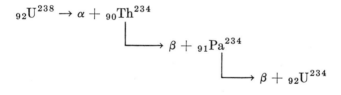

$$_{92}U^{238} \rightarrow \alpha + {}_{90}Th^{234}$$
$$\longrightarrow \beta + {}_{91}Pa^{234}$$
$$\longrightarrow \beta + {}_{92}U^{234}$$

The very existence of chains of radioactive decay among the heavy elements was indirect evidence of isotopy. Although the chains resembled each other, they also exhibited characteristic radioactive lifetimes which demonstrated their independence. As each chain extends at least from thorium to lead, the evidence for isotopes among the heavy elements was overwhelming. Soddy's remark antedated Thomson's positive-ray mass spectroscopy, so he must be credited with the discovery of isotopes. However, it was Thomson who discovered the existence of isotopes of the light elements and of stable isotopes, and who obtained the first accurate mass values.

The fact that electron emission in β-decay is always accompanied by a chemical change indicates that these electrons are in some way different from the ones which may be removed from an atom by ionization. In the latter process the chemical nature of the emitter does *not* change. The distinction between the two kinds of electrons was only clarified with the advent of the nuclear atom: the β-ray electrons come from inside the nucleus, the ionization electrons from outside (see Section 11).

8. Alpha and beta ray spectra. In using alpha particles or beta rays as projectiles for probing the interior of atoms, it was essential to know not only their nature but also the velocities with which they are projected. These velocities could be measured by the standard deflection techniques described in Sections 3 and 4, once the specific charge of the particle was known. The investigation of the distribution of velocities of the α-rays and β-rays from natural radioactive atoms forms the subject of α- and β-ray spectroscopy.

In the experiments of Rutherford and his co-workers which determined the specific charge of α-particles, no velocity selection was employed. None was necessary because each group of α-particles happens to be emitted with nearly uniform velocity. The particles therefore created only one discrete spot (or at most a few) on the detecting screen or photographic plate used in the experiments. Rutherford and Robinson determined, for example, that the velocity of the α-particles from radium C was 1.922×10^9 cm/sec [22].

The original experiments were not particularly designed for accurate velocity measurement. However, the focusing techniques of mass spectroscopy were quickly applied to the problem of determining the velocity spectrum. Rosenblum, and also Rutherford and Robinson, applied 180° focusing methods to the analysis of the velocity spectrum. According to

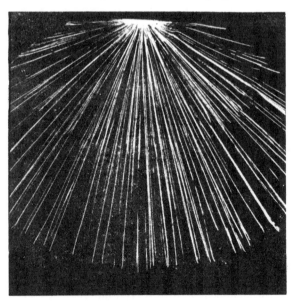

FIG. 3–8.   Cloud-chamber photograph of α-particle tracks from thorium $(C + C')$.   (Reprinted by permission from Rutherford, Chadwick, and Ellis, *Radiations from Radioactive Substances*, Cambridge University Press, 1930.)

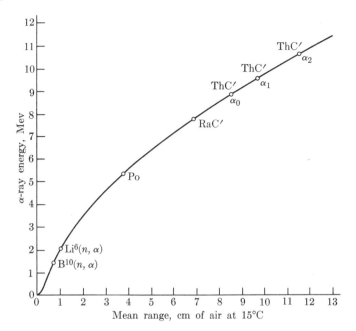

FIG. 3–9. Range-energy curve for α-particle in air.

Eq. (3–10), for a given specific charge the diameter of the semicircle is directly proportional to the velocity of the particle. The technique therefore furnishes a convenient velocity spectrometer.

Other methods for measuring the velocity of α-particles utilize the fact that the particles lose kinetic energy as they pass through matter. In solids they are stopped in a relatively short distance; in gases their range can easily be made visible by means of cloud-chamber techniques. An early cloud chamber picture showing the tracks of α-particles from a sample of thorium* is reproduced in Fig. 3–8; two distinct characteristic ranges can be identified. A definite relation exists between the velocity at any point on the track and the range from there to the end of the track (residual range). For α-particles of intermediate energies, Geiger found empirically that the residual range was approximately proportional to the cube of the velocity. Unfortunately, no such simple law holds over a very wide velocity spectrum. The range-energy and the range-velocity relations for α-particles, as well as for other charged particles, have been much investigated. A typical range-energy curve is shown in Fig. 3–9. The explanation of the relation between energy and range is quite complicated; for present purposes the relationship may as well be considered completely empirical. After such a range-energy relation has been estab-

---

* Thorium $(C + C')$.

lished, it can be used to measure the velocity of an α-particle, provided the accuracy required is not too great.

Beta rays present a very different problem. Unlike α-particles, the β-rays from a given decay are not concentrated at a few well-defined and characteristic velocities. It was determined quite early that β-rays are emitted over a wide range of velocities. In 1909 Hahn and Meitner found two distinct groups of β-rays in the velocity spectrum of radium. During the years 1910–1912 Von Bahr, Hahn, and Meitner used deflection methods, with apparatus similar to that employed by Rutherford and Robinson in their α-particle experiments, to demonstrate the existence of numerous groups of electrons in β-ray spectra. Danysz then introduced the focusing spectrograph for more accurate study, and this technique was developed by Rutherford and Robinson into an accurate tool. Soon the existence of numerous characteristic lines was established.

The line spectra, as it turns out, are not the direct product of a radio-active decay. In 1914 Rutherford, Robinson, and Rawlinson showed that similar line spectra could be produced by sending γ-rays through matter [25]. The apparatus employed was a glass tube containing radon, with thin foils of various metals wrapped around it. The velocities of the electrons leaving the tube were measured by means of the focusing spectrograph. The glass and foil were thick enough to stop many of the β-rays from the radon and caused enough straggling in the others to make the characteristic radon lines disappear. Nonetheless, distinct line spectra of electrons were observed. Rutherford correctly attributed this effect to

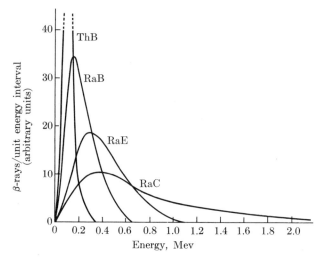

Fig. 3–10. Continuous spectra for various β-ray emitters. From Rutherford, Chadwick, and Ellis, [27].

the γ-rays emitted by radium B and radium C, which are the products of the radon β-decay. The γ-rays were able to penetrate the glass and must have transferred their energy to electrons in the metal sheath. The energies of the electron line spectra confirmed that they were caused by the radium γ-rays.

From the result of this experiment Rutherford argued that the β-ray line spectra were also most simply explained as a secondary effect, the transfer of energy from a γ-ray to an electron within the same atom. The existence of this process, called internal conversion, has been fully confirmed in modern nuclear physics. The fact that the conversion electrons are of secondary origin does not, of course, restrict their usefulness as atomic probes. It is in fact an advantage to have a group of mono-energetic electrons available in an experiment.

There are other β-rays which do not originate from the indirect mechanism just described. In fact, it was shown by Chadwick in 1914 that most of the β-rays are not contained in the characteristic lines; rather, they form a continuous spectrum [26]. Continuous β-ray spectra for some of the natural radioactive elements are shown in Fig. 3–10. It was soon established that the continuous β-ray spectrum is the primary one in the sense that these are the electrons associated with the transformation of one radioactive element into its neighbor in the periodic table. The line spectra are secondary not only because they originate from internal conversion, but also because they are not associated with a change in the chemical nature of the emitting atom.

One other fact should be noted. Although the velocity spectrum of the β-rays is continuous, it does not extend indefinitely. As the curves in Fig. 3–10 show, there is a definite upper limit to the spectrum. This limit can be measured by magnetic analysis and also shows up in experiments on the range of particles. Until the development of modern accelerators, beta rays constituted the most energetic electrons available to experimenters. The upper limit of the β-ray spectrum was therefore an important datum to take into account in the design of experiments.*

9. Evidence on atomic structure from β-ray scattering.

We now examine the evidence concerning the internal structure of atoms that was supplied by early scattering and absorption experiments. The most elementary of such evidence was the mere fact that cathode rays and β-rays could traverse relatively large quantities of matter before being absorbed.

---

* The fact that the β-ray spectrum is continuous can be utilized to infer that an additional particle, the neutrino, is emitted in the process of β-decay. The shape of the spectrum near the endpoint places an upper limit on the neutrino's mass.

Lenard, who was the first to observe this transparency, deduced from it a simple picture of the atom. If atoms were hard, tightly packed elastic spheres, he argued, then β-rays or α-particles fired at a foil of solid matter should all be scattered backwards. The fact that β-radiation is able to penetrate solid matter shows that such a hard-sphere model is untenable. Lenard drew the simplest possible conclusion. He decided that atoms must be largely vacuous; that they must consist of a certain number of small neutral particles (dynamids) with a great amount of free space between them.

Lenard's conclusion is not the only way to explain the transparency. On the macroscopic scale, there exist media which projectiles can penetrate but which do not consist largely of empty space. For example, solid objects can move freely through fluids, not only gases but also liquids which are closely packed. On the basis of this analogy it should not be surprising that a Thomson atom also permits the passage of radiation.

More can be learned from the passage of β-rays through matter than the crude fact of partial transparency. As the rays traverse the target they interact with the target atoms, presumably through electromagnetic forces, and are deflected from their original paths. The distribution in angular deflections which results when β-rays pass through a given thickness of material reflects the atomic properties in considerable detail. The measurement of such angular distributions therefore provides a sensitive check on the correctness of any atomic model.

In 1910 Thomson calculated the angular distribution to be expected when β-rays are sent through a metal foil [28]. He argued that a β-ray had to pass through many atoms in traversing the foil and was therefore scattered many times before emerging. The final direction of motion is thus determined by the composition of many deflections. The individual deflections are all independent, so the compounding must occur in a statistical manner. The study of such a process is called a *multiple-scattering* theory.

The angle through which any given β-ray is scattered in one particular atom depends on how near the ray happens to pass to the various charges present in the atom. However, for the purpose of his calculation, Thomson assumed that every β-ray is deflected through the *same* angle θ_0 each time it traverses a single atom. The value of θ_0 is an appropriate average over the possible paths through the atom, while the direction of deflection is random. Under such conditions the path of the β-ray through the target is essentially a random walk. The principal characteristic of this type of motion is, as we have seen in Chapter 2, that after the β-ray has passed through N atoms, its root-mean-square deflection is $\sqrt{N}\,\theta_0$. If n is the number of atoms per unit volume and R the radius of an atom, then the number of atoms traversed by the β-ray in traveling a distance t is

$N = \pi R^2 nt$. Consequently the rms deflection is

$$\theta_{\text{rms}} = (\pi R^2 nt)^{1/2}\theta_0. \tag{3-17}$$

Since θ_0 is velocity dependent, (3–17) holds only if the rays are not appreciably reduced in velocity while passing through the target. This condition is satisfied as long as the target is fairly thin.

The statistical theory predicts not only the rms-deflection but also the distribution around this value. As in any random-walk problem, the distribution is Gaussian, with a width proportional to $\sqrt{N}$. Provided that θ_{rms} is small, the number of rays scattered through angles between θ and $\theta + d\theta$ is

$$I(\theta)\, d\theta = (\text{const})e^{-\theta^2/\theta_{\text{rms}}^2}\, \theta\, d\theta. \tag{3-18}$$

The factor $\theta\, d\theta$ on the right-hand side represents the element of area $\sin \theta\, d\theta$ after the small-angle approximation is made. Within the same approximation, the fraction of β-rays scattered through angles greater than θ is

$$p(\theta) = \exp\left(\frac{-\theta^2}{\theta_{\text{rms}}^2}\right). \tag{3-19}$$

Thomson calculated the mean atomic deflection θ_0 to be expected on the basis of his model of the atom. He considered first the angular deflection of the incident ray caused by an encounter with a single atomic electron. The problem of motion under the influence of an inverse-square force is familiar from astronomy; when the particle is unbound, the orbit is known to be a hyperbola. In the present problem the situation is complicated somewhat by the fact that the particle being deflected is as heavy as the one which causes the deflection. The scatterer therefore cannot be assumed to remain fixed. The motion is discussed in Appendix 3. The result is that the β-ray is deflected through an angle θ determined by the relation

$$\tan \theta = \frac{2e^2}{mv^2 p}, \tag{3-20}$$

where v is the velocity of the incident ray and p the impact parameter, the perpendicular distance from the scattering electron to the original path of the β-ray (see Fig. 3–11).

It should be remarked that Eq. (3–20) neglects the effect of relativity, which is quite considerable for the energies at which the experiments were carried out. Even though the theory of relativity had been in existence for several years, Thomson did not take it into account.

For β-rays of reasonably high energy, large-angle deflections occur only when the impact parameter is very small. For example, if the velocity is

10^{10} cm/sec, an impact parameter of 2.5×10^{-10} cm is required to give a deflection of 1°. Such a close collision must be very rare. If the deflection is assumed *a priori* to be small it can be calculated from a very simple argument, which is presented in Appendix 3. The result is of course the same as Eq. (3–20), with tan θ replaced by θ. Making this replacement must cause a negligible error in the calculation of the mean deflection θ_0.

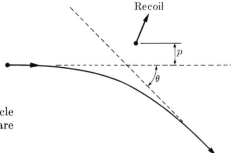

FIG. 3–11. Deflection of a particle by one of equal mass (inverse-square force).

Thomson treated the passage of the beta ray through the atom as a succession of Z_E separate collisions, where Z_E is the number of atomic electrons. In each collision the deflection was assumed to be given by (3–20); the values of p, and therefore of θ, of course vary from one collision to another. However, Thomson again replaced all the deflection angles by a single value obtained by averaging over all possible paths and impact parameters; the direction of each deflection was taken as random. Under these assumptions the path of the β-ray through the atom is another random walk, in which the rms deflection, θ_1, is proportional to the square root of the number of electrons. After the averaging process is carried out (with some approximations), the result is

$$\theta_1 = \sqrt{\frac{384}{25}} \left(\frac{e^2}{mv^2 R} \right) Z_E^{1/2}. \qquad (3\text{–}21)$$

Equation (3–21) gives only the deflection caused by the electrons; the effect of the positive fluid must also be considered. The deflection produced by a uniformly charged sphere of radius R and charge $Z_E e$ is given by an expression similar to (3–20). The root mean square deflection caused by the fluid, averaged over all impact parameters, turns out to be

$$\theta_2 = \frac{\pi}{4} \left(\frac{e^2}{mv^2 R} \right) Z_E. \qquad (3\text{–}22)$$

This must be combined with the contribution of the electrons, Eq. (3–21). Since the two contributions are independent, their mean square values must be added and the rms deflection caused by a single atom is

$$\theta_0 = (\theta_1^2 + \theta_2^2)^{1/2}. \tag{3-23}$$

Combining Eqs. (3–21) through (3–23) with (3–17), one obtains an expression for the final rms deflection:

$$\theta_{\text{rms}} = \frac{e^2}{mv^2} \left(\frac{384}{25} Z_E + \frac{\pi^2}{16} Z_E^2 \right)^{1/2} (\pi n t)^{1/2}. \tag{3-24}$$

Since the number of atoms per unit volume is known, θ_{rms} is, according to this theory, a measure of the number of electrons per atom, Z_E.

Shortly after Thomson had presented his theory, Crowther [29] measured the angular distribution in the scattering of β-rays from various foils. The resolution in Crowther's experiments was not good enough to permit a detailed comparison with the angular distribution predicted by Eqs. (3–18) and (3–24). However, several predictions based on this distribution could be checked. Let Φ be the angle beyond which half of the incident particles are scattered. From equations (3–19) and (3–24), it follows that Φ is of the form

$$\Phi^2 = (\text{const}) \frac{nt}{T^2}, \tag{3-25}$$

where T is the kinetic energy of the betas and the constant depends only on Z_E. According to Eq. (3–25), for a given target material Φ ought to be proportional to the square root of the target thickness and inversely proportional to the kinetic energy of the incident betas. This prediction was experimentally verified, within the accuracy of Crowther's data. The result appeared to lend support to Thomson's atomic model, as well as to the validity of the multiple-scattering theory. However, it was subsequently shown by Rutherford that the same relation (3–25) is predicted also by a single-scattering theory and a nuclear atom; only the value of the constant is different [see Eq. (3–38).]

From the experimental values of θ_{rms}, the electron numbers Z_E could be calculated by means of Eq. (3–24). When Crowther interpreted his results in this manner, he concluded that, approximately,

$$Z_E \approx 3A, \tag{3-26}$$

where A is the mass number of the atom involved. The conclusion that Z_E is proportional to A agreed with the earlier estimates of Thomson already cited (pp. 67). However, the actual relation (3–26) turned out to be only very qualitatively correct. It did not agree with the estimates provided by x ray and α-ray scattering data, nor is it consistent with the modern picture of the atom, according to which Z_E is about half of A, (somewhat less for heavy atoms).

It must be borne in mind that Crowther's experiments were fairly crude. However, Thomson's theory also contained several questionable features. Not the least of these was the statistical treatment of the deflections caused by electrons within a single atom. Even according to Thomson's own model, the atomic electrons are arranged in systematic arrays, and for such an array Eq. (3–21), based on random averaging, may be considerably in error.

A direct test of the multiple-scattering hypothesis is to measure the dependence on target thickness of $F_<(\theta)$, the fraction of β-rays scattered through angles *less* than θ. Equations (3–17) and (3–19) predict that $F_<(\theta)$ is of the form

$$F_<(\theta) = 1 - e^{-\gamma\theta^2/t}, \tag{3-27}$$

where γ is a constant. The behavior of (3–27) as a function of thickness is characteristic of a multiple-scattering theory. Crowther attempted to verify this predicted behavior by passing the beam of β-particles through an aperture which subtended an angle of 36° with the scattering foil. He asserted that his results were in accord with Eq. (3–27) for small thicknesses of foil material. However, other experiments on β-ray scattering, for example those of Madsen in 1909, were not in agreement with Crowther's conclusion. They indicated more nearly a linear relation of the form

$$F_<(\theta) = 1 - \alpha t, \tag{3-28}$$

with α a constant whose value depends on θ. Such a relation is not to be expected from a multiple-scattering process; it is characteristic of single scattering, as we shall see later on. The discrepancies between these results and Crowther's were not fully resolved until much later, when it was shown that β-ray scattering exhibits both single- and multiple-scattering features.

Beta-ray experiments have been performed many times since the ones just discussed. Fast electrons are still being used to unravel the structure of atoms, and very recently the technique has been applied in the investigation of the charge distribution within the nucleus.

X-rays provided another probe of great usefulness in studying the structure of atoms. Although a detailed discussion of the action of x-rays is postponed to the next volume, it should be mentioned here that they were used at about the same time as the β-ray evidence to give an independent evaluation of the number of electrons in atoms. From early experiments on the scattering of x-rays, Thomson had concluded that the number of electrons per atom was approximately the same as the atomic weight. More accurate measurements by Barkla in 1911 indicated that, for light elements, the number of electrons was closer to half the atomic mass number. The x-ray evidence was somewhat more precise and its interpretation less open to criticism than the conclusions from β-ray scattering.* The x-ray and β-ray evidence did agree qualitatively that the number of electrons is of the order of the atomic mass number and approximately proportional to it.

10. Alpha-particle evidence on atomic structure; the Rutherford atom.
In 1911 Rutherford published his fundamental paper [30] which presented evidence that the atom is radically different from the models envisaged by Thomson and Lenard. Rutherford's argument was based on alpha-particle scattering experiments performed by Geiger [31] and by Geiger and Marsden [32].

The scattering of alpha particles differs from that of electrons in at least one important respect. Because the alpha has such a large mass, it is virtually undeflected by the atomic electrons. Simple considerations of energy and momentum conservation show that in a collision between an energetic α-particle and a free electron the velocity of the alpha particle is changed by an extremely small amount. The atomic electrons behave essentially as free particles since their binding energies are so much smaller than the kinetic energy of the α-particles. Experiments on alpha-particle scattering, therefore, constitute a direct probe of the distribution of the massive positively charged component of the atom.

If the Thomson model were correct, the multiple-scattering theory described in the last section should apply also to alpha-particle scattering. The angular distribution ought to be of the form (3–18), where θ_{rms} is given by an expression like (3–24) but without the electron contribution. However, Rutherford noticed one important feature of the experimental results which was quite different: there were far too many large-angle deflections to be accounted for by the multiple-scattering theory. This was the chief datum upon which the nuclear model was founded.

Using as a target a gold foil about 4×10^{-5} cm thick, Geiger had found that the angle Φ, beyond which half the α-particles were scattered, was approximately 1°. According to the multiple-scattering theory, the mean square angle of deflection is related to Φ by Eq. (3–19):

$$\theta_{rms}^2 = \frac{\Phi^2}{\ln 2} = 1.4 \text{ (degrees)}^2. \tag{3–29}$$

Since the foil was about 1500 atoms thick, this result implied (again according to the multiple-scattering theory) that the mean deflection caused

---

* Actually the theory on which Barkla's results were based is also of limited validity. However, he fortunately employed x-rays of wavelengths for which the theory happens to be quite good. The subject is discussed in Volume 2, Chapter 2.

by a single gold atom was

$$\theta_0 = \theta_{\text{rms}}/\sqrt{1500} \approx 0.03°.$$

With such a small value of θ_0, the chance that an α-particle undergoes a large total deflection is minute. Even if each atom were to scatter the α-particle in the same direction (a totally unlikely possibility), the overall deflection would be only 45°. Nevertheless, Geiger and Marsden found that approximately one α-particle in 20,000 was deflected through an angle greather than 90°. Though this is not a large fraction, it is immense when compared to the prediction of the multiple-scattering theory. Equation (3–19) would give for this fraction the value 10^{-2430}, an unimaginably small number. (Recall that the number of particles in the universe is only of the order of 10^{80}.)

Other experiments of Geiger and Marsden showed that α-particles were also scattered backward by thick targets to an extent far greater than could be explained by a multiple-scattering theory. It may appear at first sight that, if the target is sufficiently thick, an expression like Eq. (3–18) will lead to almost complete backscattering (since θ_{rms}^2 is proportional to t). This conclusion is, however, fallacious. With a mean deflection of 0.03° in each collision, an α-particle would have to pass through 9×10^6 atoms, on the average, in order to attain a total deflection of 90°. Such a large number of atoms implies a path length of about 0.3 cm, which is far greater than the range of α-particles in gold. Long before the particles had experienced the required number of collisions, they would have lost their energy and come to rest.

On the basis of these considerations, Rutherford concluded that at least some of the α-particles had been deflected through 90° or more in a *single* collision. Thomson's model, with its positive fluid which fills the entire atom, was totally incapable of accounting for such an occurrence. The reason is simple enough: to deflect something as heavy as an α-particle by 90° requires a very strong field, which the distributed positive fluid just does not provide. Rutherford suggested that the massive positive charge was, instead, concentrated in a very small region at the center of the atom.* Such a distribution leads to a large-angle deflection whenever the α-particle happens to pass through the intense field in the close vicinity of the nucleus.

The nuclear hypothesis is not the only possible way to account for the observed backscattering. One might, for example, try to salvage the Thomson atom by postulating that a strong surface force acts on the

---

* The idea of a small positive nucleus appeared first in the "Saturnian" model proposed by Nagaoka in 1904 [33]. At that time there was no evidence to support such a conjecture. See also the remarks by Lodge (p. 66).

α-particles and causes them to be reflected as though they had struck a rigid sphere. This surface force might have the same origin as the force which must be invoked in any case to hold the positive fluid together. A completely rigid-sphere behavior would not be satisfactory, since it would predict much *more* backscattering than was experimentally observed. However, some modification of this model could undoubtedly be constructed in which the α-particles are partially reflected from a surface layer; by adjusting the parameters, any desired amount of backscattering could be obtained. The correctness of Rutherford's hypothesis was established only by the quantitative agreement of its predictions with the scattering experiments to be described presently.

It is not hard to estimate roughly how small a nucleus must be in order to be able to deflect an α-particle through a right angle. As long as the α-particle remains outside the nucleus, the latter acts as a point charge and the trajectory is a hyperbola. (The heavy nucleus can be considered to remain fixed.) The derivation in Appendix 3 shows that the deflection angle is given by

$$\tan \frac{\theta}{2} = \frac{2Z_N e^2}{mv^2 p} , \qquad (3\text{-}30)$$

where $Z_N e$ is the nuclear charge. As before, p is the impact parameter.

It is convenient to introduce the parameter b, the closest possible distance of approach of the α-particle to the nucleus. The closest approach occurs when the α-particle is aimed directly toward the center of the nucleus and is turned around by the collision. Under the assumption that the α-particle does not enter the nucleus, an expression for b can be obtained directly from the conservation of energy:

$$b = \frac{4Z_N e^2}{mv^2} . \qquad (3\text{-}31)$$

When the collision is not "head-on," the distance of closest approach, a, is greater than b. It is a matter of geometry to show (see Problem 3-3) that

$$a = \frac{b}{2} \left(1 + \csc \frac{\theta}{2} \right) . \qquad (3\text{-}32)$$

In Geiger's experiment Z_N was about 80, and the α-particle velocity about 2×10^9 cm/sec. With these values, Eq. (3-31) gives $b = 3 \times 10^{-12}$ cm. For a 90° deflection, Eqs. (3-30) and (3-32) give

$$p_{90°} = 1.5 \times 10^{-12} \text{ cm}, \qquad (3\text{-}33a)$$

$$a_{90°} = 3.6 \times 10^{-12} \text{ cm}. \qquad (3\text{-}33b)$$

If the nuclear radius were equal to $a_{90°}$, then in a 90° collision the α-particle would just graze the edge of the nucleus (Fig. 3–12). If the radius were much greater than $a_{90°}$, an α-particle with the same impact parameter $p_{90°}$ would penetrate the nucleus. While it was inside, this particle would be subject to weaker forces, and its total deflection would be less than 90°, just as in the Thomson atom. Hence, one can argue that the value of $a_{90°}$ furnishes a rough upper bound for the radius of the gold nucleus. (A better argument is given in the next section.) The radius could, of course, be anything smaller than $a_{90°}$, so far as the present argument is concerned. The actual nuclear radii turn out to be smaller, by a factor of about three, than the values given by this simple estimate; they are, then, about 10,000 times smaller than the radii of atoms. In this respect Lenard's conjecture was correct: the atom is largely empty space. Lenard, however, had pictured the atom as being composed of tiny neutral particles distributed throughout its volume. His atom has no nucleus.

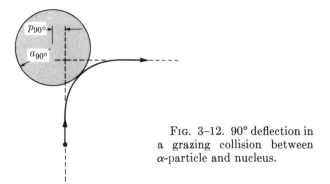

FIG. 3–12. 90° deflection in a grazing collision between α-particle and nucleus.

The calculation just presented yields also an estimate of the probability for a deflection of 90° or more. Such a deflection occurs whenever the impact parameter is less than the value given in Eq. (3–33a). The probability that p be this small in a single collision is the ratio between the areas $\pi p_{90°}^2$ and πR^2 (where R is the atomic radius), or approximately 10^{-8}. Evidently, the chance that a single α-particle would experience two such large deflections is negligibly small. Therefore, the total probability for a deflection of 90° or more in passing through a foil 1500 atoms thick can be estimated as 1500×10^{-8}. This result is in qualitative agreement with the observation of Geiger and Marsden on the fraction of such large-angle deflections.

According to the nuclear model, essentially all the large-angle deflections must be the result of single collisions. A direct test of this conclusion is the dependence of the scattering on target thickness. If single scattering is indeed the primary mechanism, the number of

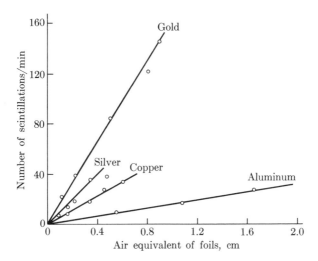

FIG. 3–13. Variation of α-particle scattering with target thickness (fixed angle). From Geiger and Marsden [32].

particles scattered through a given angle θ ought to be directly proportional to the target thickness, except for very small angles. The multiple-scattering theory, as we have seen in the last section, predicts a very different dependence on thickness [Eq. (3–27)].

The dependence of scattered intensity on foil thickness was measured by Geiger and Marsden as part of a comprehensive check of the Rutherford theory [34]. Most of the data were taken at a scattering angle of approximately 25°; the results are shown in Fig. 3–13. The observed linearity furnished strong support for the single-scattering hypothesis.

From the arguments already presented, it is straightforward to derive the angular distribution predicted by the Rutherford theory. Equation (3–30) gives the scattering angle as a function of impact parameter. An α-particle which passes a given nucleus with an impact parameter between p and $p + dp$ is scattered through an angle between the corresponding θ and $\theta + d\theta$. The probability that p is within this range in a given atom is the ratio of the areas

$$\frac{2\pi p \, dp}{\pi R^2}.$$

(3–34)

The probability that a collision of just this type occurs once while the α-particle passes through a target of thickness t is given by (3–34) multiplied by the number of atoms traversed, $\pi R^2 nt$. Hence the probability that an individual alpha particle is scattered through an angle between

TABLE 3–5

ANGULAR DISTRIBUTION IN α-PARTICLE SCATTERING
from Geiger and Marsden [34]

Angle of deflection, θ	$\csc^4 \frac{1}{2}\theta$	SILVER		GOLD	
		Number of scintillations, N	$\dfrac{N}{\csc^4 \frac{1}{2}\theta}$	Number of scintillations, N	$\dfrac{N}{\csc^4 \frac{1}{2}\theta}$
150°	1.15	22.2	19.3	33.1	28.8
135	1.38	27.4	19.8	43.0	31.2
120	1.79	33.0	18.4	51.9	29.0
105	2.53	47.3	18.7	69.5	27.5
75	7.25	136	18.8	211	29.1
60	16.0	320	20.0	477	29.8
45	46.6	989	21.2	1,435	30.8
37.5	93.7	1,760	18.8	3,300	35.3
30	223	5,260	23.6	7,800	35.0
22.5	690	20,300	29.4	27,300	39.6
15	3445	105,400	30.6	132,000	38.4
30	223	5.3	0.024	3.1	0.014
22.5	690	16.6	0.024	8.4	0.012
15	3445	93.0	0.027	48.2	0.014
10	17330	508	0.029	200	0.0115
7.5	54650	1,710	0.031	607	0.011
5	276300	—	—	3,320	0.012

θ and $\theta + d\theta$ is, using Eq. (3–30),

$$G(\theta)\,d\theta = 2\pi ntp\,dp$$
$$= 2\pi nt\left(\frac{2Z_N e^2}{mv^2}\right)^2 \frac{\cos(\theta/2)\,d(\theta/2)}{\sin^3(\theta/2)}. \qquad (3\text{–}35)$$

Equation (3–35) gives also the fraction of an incident beam scattered through angles between θ and $\theta + d\theta$. It is customary to give the result in terms of intensity per solid angle, since this is the quantity measured experimentally. Defining $F(\theta)$ by

$$G(\theta)\,d\theta \equiv F(\theta)\,d\Omega = F(\theta)2\pi \sin\theta\,d\theta,$$

one obtains for $F(\theta)$ the relation

$$F(\theta) = \frac{1}{4}\,nt\left(\frac{2Z_N e^2}{mv^2}\right)^2 \csc^4 \frac{\theta}{2}, \qquad (3\text{–}36)$$

which is the famous Rutherford scattering law.

TABLE 3–6

VARIATION OF SCATTERING WITH VELOCITY
from Geiger and Marsden [34]

Range of particles (cm of air)	Relative values of $1/v^4$	Number N of scintillations	Nv^4
5.5	1.0	24.7	25
4.76	1.21	29.0	24
4.05	1.50	33.4	22
3.32	1.91	44	23
2.51	2.84	81	28
1.84	4.32	101	23
1.04	9.22	255	28

Rutherford's theory makes very definite predictions concerning the scattering, which can be directly tested by experiment. It asserts that the scattered intensity per solid angle is proportional to:

a) the thickness of the scatterer;
b) the square of the nuclear charge;
c) the inverse square of the kinetic energy of the α-particles; and
d) the angular factor $\csc^4(\theta/2)$.

In 1911 Geiger obtained a preliminary confirmation of the predicted angular distribution, and in 1913 Geiger and Marsden published the results of their long series of measurements, which experimentally verified all the consequences of the Rutherford scattering law [34]. The part of the experiment which demonstrated the linear dependence of scattered intensity on foil thickness has already been mentioned. The angular distribution was checked over a very wide range of angles, up to 150°. By interposing various thicknesses of mica between an α-source and the scattering foil, Geiger and Marsden slowed down the α-particles and were able to verify the predicted dependence of scattered intensity upon α-particle energy, within the rather limited range of velocities available. These very important results are summarized in Fig. 3–13 and Tables 3–5 and 3–6. In view of the great variation in counting rate over the range of angles and velocities measured, the agreement with the theory had to be considered excellent. After these experiments, there could be little doubt of the correctness of Rutherford's nuclear hypothesis.

The concept of nuclear charge was introduced by Rutherford's model and has no meaning independent of the model. The experimenters therefore could not expect to verify the predicted Z_N^2 dependence in the same way that they verified the other predictions of the model. However, it was possible to study the variation of the scattering with atomic *mass* by comparing the scattered intensity produced at a given angle by targets of different materials. If Z_N is assumed to be proportional to A, the Rutherford law predicts that the scattering should vary as A^2. The results of Geiger and Marsden were consistent with such a variation, although the quadratic dependence was not established with any certainty.

In principle, once the Rutherford law had been confirmed, the magnitude of the nuclear charge should have been obtainable from Geiger and Marsden's data. However, for such a determination it was necessary to compare the intensity of the beam scattered in a given direction with the intensity of the incident beam. The scattered intensity was measured by counting scintillations produced on a zinc sulfide screen. The incident beam was too strong to be counted in this fashion and had to be calibrated in other ways. (For example, from the associated γ-ray activity.) As a result, the absolute value of the ratio I_{sc}/I_{inc} was subject to a rather large uncertainty, even though the dependence of I_{sc} on scattering angle, incident velocity, and target thickness could be accurately measured. When Geiger and Marsden tried to deduce values of the nuclear charges from their data (assuming the validity of Rutherford's formula), they could conclude only that Z_N is approximately equal to $A/2$, within $\pm 20\%$. Accurate determinations of the nuclear charges by means of α-particle scattering were not achieved until 1920, by Chadwick. (See the following section.)

The probability that an α-particle is scattered through an angle greater than θ is obtained by integrating Eq. (3–35) between θ and π. The result is

$$p(\theta) = \frac{1}{4}\ \pi nt \left(\frac{4Z_N e^2}{mv^2}\right)^2 \cot^2 \frac{\theta}{2}. \qquad (3\text{–}37)$$

For small enough θ, the probability as given by Eq. (3–37) exceeds unity. This absurd result reflects the fact that the assumption of single scattering cannot be valid for arbitrarily small deflection angles. The Coulomb force of every nucleus, no matter how distant, causes some small deflection; consequently there must be an angle below which multiple-scattering effects are important. Indeed, Geiger interpreted his early experiments [31] according to multiple scattering theory; for the small-angle part of the distribution, there was no difficulty with such an interpretation. (See Fig. 3–14.)

A simple argument may be used to estimate the angle below which multiple-scattering corrections are to be expected. If $p(\theta)$ is the probability that a particle is scattered once through an angle as large as θ while passing through the target, then the chance that it experiences two

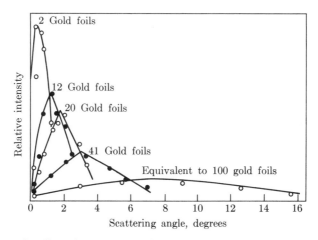

FIG. 3–14. Small-angle part of the distribution in the scattering of α-particles from gold. These data are consistent with a multiple-scattering interpretation. From Geiger [31].

such deflections is $[p(\theta)]^2$. As long as $p(\theta) \ll 1$, multiple scattering may therefore be ignored. The angle Φ, for which $p = \frac{1}{2}$, is a rough measure of the frontier between the single- and multiple-scattering regions. When Φ is small enough to justify the small-angle approximation (as it almost always is) the single-scattering theory gives, from Eq. (3–37),

$$\Phi^2 = 2\pi n t \left(\frac{4Z_N e^2}{mv^2}\right)^2. \tag{3–38}$$

We note in passing that this expression is proportional to nt/T^2, just like Thomson's multiple-scattering formula (3–25). It follows that Crowther's observation of a $t^{1/2}/T$ dependence for Φ in β-ray scattering, described in the preceding section, does not justify a multiple-scattering interpretation of the data. Rutherford in his original paper successfully explained Crowther's findings on the assumption that, in β-ray scattering too, the large-angle deflections are the result of single collisions.

For a complete description of the small-angle scattering of α-particles, one additional factor must be taken into account, namely the effect of atomic electrons. We have already argued that an individual electron, because of its small mass, cannot appreciably deflect a rapidly moving α-particle. However, all the electrons taken together serve to partially screen the field of the nucleus from the incident particle. The screening is effective only when the impact parameter is comparable with the distances at which the electrons are found; the electrons therefore influence only very-small-angle deflections. Problem 3–4 provides an estimate of the angle at which the effect becomes important.

11. The proton-electron model. Rutherford's original paper did not present a complete atomic model. The α-scattering evidence argued only for the existence of a nucleus and did not even specify the sign of the nuclear charge. Since Eq. (3–36) involves only Z_N^2, a negative nucleus gives precisely the same angular distribution as a positive one. Clearly, however, the negative nucleus would lead to serious difficulties.

Granted a positively charged nucleus, the remainder of the atom must consist of electrons sufficient in number to balance the nuclear charge. Since, according to Earnshaw's theorem,* no configuration of point charges can be in static equilibrium, the extranuclear electrons must be in motion. Therefore the existence of the nucleus leads naturally to a solar-system model of the atom, although such a model was not insisted on at first by Rutherford.

Further investigation of the composition of the nucleus required, first of all, a precise knowledge of the nuclear charges. In 1913 Van den Broek suggested that Z_N might be equal to the atomic number Z, deduced from the position of the element in the periodic table. (Ambiguities in some of the Z values had been recently resolved by the very accurate x-ray data of Moseley; this work is discussed in Volume 2.) Even though Geiger and Marsden's early estimate of $Z_N (\approx A/2)$ was somewhat higher than Z, the experimental uncertainty was large enough to allow the possibility that the two quantities might be equal. Definite confirmation of Van den Broek's hypothesis was provided by the accurate measurements of Chadwick already mentioned [35]. Chadwick obtained the values 29.3, 46.3, and 77.4 (in units of the electronic charge) for the nuclear charges of copper, silver, and platinum, respectively, with an estimated accuracy of 1 or 2%. Moseley's values of Z for these elements were 29, 47, and 78.

The confirmation of Van den Broek's hypothesis, together with the mass-spectroscopic data discussed in Section 3–4, led to a simple and appealing model of atomic composition. The mass data, it will be recalled, showed that all ions have masses which are approximately integral multiples of that of the proton.† It seemed reasonable to suppose, therefore, that atoms contain protons. The simplest possible atom is one composed entirely of protons and electrons. Such a model eventually had to be abandoned, but for a long time it furnished a satisfactory basis for the description of all known atomic and nuclear phenomena.

Since the electron's mass is minute, almost the entire mass of an atom (according to this model) comes from the protons. It follows that the nucleus of an atom of mass number A contains A protons. If the net

---

* Volume 2, Chapter 2.

† Various names were proposed for the hydrogen ion, among them "hydron" and "hydrion." The name "proton" was adopted at a meeting of the British Association in 1920.

charge is to be Z, there must also be $A - Z$ electrons in the nucleus. The number of extranuclear electrons is then Z, and the total number of electrons is A. This conclusion is not inconsistent with the rough estimates of electron numbers based on β-ray and x-ray scattering, discussed earlier.

The separation of atomic electrons into two types, nuclear and extranuclear, appeared sensible for a number of other reasons. The nuclear electrons, being in close proximity to a large positive charge, would have a very high binding energy. The order of magnitude of this binding must be Ze^2/R, where R is the nuclear radius; for $R \sim 10^{-12}$ cm, the binding energy is of the order of 10^6 ev. Thus only the extranuclear electrons would be subject to ionization in ordinary experiments. For example helium, with $A = 4$, $Z = 2$, has, on the proton-electron model, two nuclear and two extranuclear electrons. And indeed, whereas the ionization energies of the first two electrons in helium are 24.6 and 54.4 ev respectively, no further electrons can be removed by ordinary means. Similarly in lithium ($A = 7$, $Z = 3$) only three electrons can be ionized.

The distinctive nature of β-ray electrons, discussed in Section 7, could also be understood if they were assumed to originate within the nucleus. This hypothesis accounts both for the high β-ray energies, and for the fact that a chemical change always accompanies β-ray emission (since the nuclear charge is thereby changed).

The arguments against a proton-electron model are quite subtle, and the model was not definitely disproved for a long time. However, as early as 1920 it was suggested independently by Harkins, Masson, and Rutherford that a proton and electron in close association might form a single tightly bound unit which behaves essentially as a neutral particle of approximately protonic mass. If electrons and protons are both present within a nucleus, at very small separations, the probability for formation of such a composite particle ought to be quite large. Much later, in 1932, the neutron was identified by Chadwick and subsequently proved to be a fundamental constituent of the nucleus. According to the proton-neutron model, a nucleus contains Z protons and $A - Z$ neutrons, and the only electrons in the atom are outside the nucleus. The neutron is not, of course, a simple combination of proton and electron, as envisaged in the early speculations. When it decays into proton and electron an additional neutral particle, the neutrino, is given off. But the germ of the early idea proved to be correct.

12. The law of force and the size of atomic nuclei. The Rutherford scattering formula was based on the assumption that the force between α-particle and nucleus is given exactly by Coulomb's law for point charges. This assumption could not be expected to be valid for arbitrarily small separations. If the nucleus is spherically symmetric, Gauss's law allows us to replace it by a point charge at its center, so long as the alpha-particle remains completely outside. When the separation approaches the nuclear radius, deviations from an inverse-square law of force are to be anticipated for any of several reasons:

(a) The distribution of charge within the nucleus may be rearranged or "polarized" by the repulsion of the nearby α-particle. The field of such a nonspherical distribution is not that of a point charge.

(b) Even if the nuclear charge is somehow rigidly maintained in spherical symmetry, part of the charge is shielded when the α-particle is inside the nucleus. The effective charge is then smaller than the total nuclear charge.

(c) Coulomb's law itself may not be valid at extremely small distances. All the previous experiments on which Coulomb's law was based had involved distances much greater than 10^{-12} cm. There was no evidence that the inverse-square dependence still holds at these minute separations.

(d) There might exist an additional force, entirely apart from the Coulomb force, which acts only at very small distances. The presence of such a force is in fact demanded by the very existence of the nucleus. If, as believed, there are protons present in the nucleus, these protons repel one another very strongly. A competing strongly attractive force must therefore be present to prevent the constituents of the nucleus from flying apart. Since the incident α-particle also contains protons, the same short-range attraction ought to act on it.

(e) Finally, the possibility had to be considered that the laws of classical mechanics might not be valid for the description of phenomena on such a minute scale. (See the remark at the end of this chapter about the classical description of scattering.)

For all these reasons, deviations from the Rutherford scattering formula might be expected when the incident alpha particles closely approach or actually enter the nucleus. Conversely, observation of deviations from the Rutherford formula should give direct information concerning the size of the nucleus. Equations (3–31) and (3–32) indicate that the distance of closest approach varies inversely with the kinetic energy of the alpha particle and decreases with the angle of deflection. Therefore, the deviations should be most apparent in the scattering of high-energy alpha particles, and particularly in the backward direction.

Any deviation from a pure inverse-square force affects the dependence of the scattering both on angle of deflection and on the alpha-particle velocity. Darwin in 1914 calculated the scattering caused by a force proportional to $1/r^p$. He showed [36] that the scattered intensity varies with velocity as

$$\left(\frac{1}{v^2}\right)^{2/(p-1)}. \tag{3-39}$$

The results of Geiger and Marsden already quoted (see Table 3–6) were consistent with $p = 2$. In his experiments of 1920 Chadwick carefully tested the dependence of the scattering on α-particle velocity, using platinum as a target [35]. Again no evidence was obtained for deviations from the Coulomb law. The fastest alpha particles in Chadwick's experiment came within about 7×10^{-12} cm of the nucleus; this distance was therefore established as an upper bound for the nuclear radius of platinum. Chadwick's results were extended by Rutherford and Chadwick in 1925 [37]. Working with alpha particles scattered through 135° by the nuclei of silver, gold, platinum, and copper, they once again found no evidence of deviation from the Coulomb law. This experiment showed that the nuclear radii are not greater than 3.2×10^{-12} cm for gold, 2×10^{-12} cm for silver, and 1.2×10^{-12} cm for copper. The angular distributions in all the experiments were also consistent with the $\csc^4 (\theta/2)$ dependence predicted by the Rutherford formula.

The best that the experiments with heavy nuclei could do was to put upper limits on the nuclear sizes. To investigate still smaller separations would have required more energetic alpha particles, which unfortunately were not available at the time. For this reason Rutherford and his co-workers turned their attention to the lighter nuclei, which the available alpha particles could approach more closely.

Bieler [38] in 1924 measured the angular dependence of the scattering from aluminum ($Z = 13$) and magnesium ($Z = 12$), using alpha particles from radium ($v = 1.9 \times 10^9$ cm/sec) and from polonium ($v = 1.6 \times 10^9$ cm/sec). He compared the scattered intensity in various angular intervals with the intensity predicted by the Rutherford formula.* Bieler's results are summarized in Table 3–7. It is clear that a deviation exists at all except the forward angles, and that the deviations increase with the scattering angle. Moreover, the direction of the deviations is consistent with what one would expect from an additional attractive force, which cancels part of the Coulomb repulsion, as predicted by argument (d) above.

Bieler was able to measure only the total intensity in rather broad angular regions. His data therefore do not permit an accurate specification of the angles at which the deviations begin. However, these angles can be roughly estimated as 20° for the fast α-particles and 50° for the slow ones. The corresponding distances of closest approach are, using Eqs. (3–31) and (3–32), 1.7×10^{-12} cm and 1.3×10^{-12} cm, respectively. Presumably, these distances constitute a measure of the sum of the radii of the α-particle and the aluminum nucleus.

---

*For the scattering by light elements, the target nucleus cannot be assumed to remain fixed, and the Rutherford formula must be accordingly modified. The modifications are discussed in Appendix 3.

TABLE 3–7

ANGULAR DISTRIBUTION IN SCATTERING OF α-PARTICLES
BY ALUMINUM AND MAGNESIUM

Measured by Bieler [38]. The scattering from gold was used as a standard.

(a) Alpha particles from RaC, mean range = 6.6 cm		
Angular region	Ratio of observed scattering/Rutherford formula	
	Al	Mg
17.6°–23.6°	1.00 ± .03	1.02 ± .03
23.7 –44.2	0.94 ± .02	
43.9 –59.7	0.78 ± .02	0.90 ± .03
60.3 –99.5	0.71 ± .02	0.69 ± .02
(b) Alpha particles from Po, mean range = 3.0 cm		
43.9 –59.7	1.00 ± .03	1.05 ± .06
60.3 –99.5	0.93 ± .03	0.79 ± .08

Similar results were obtained from measurement of the energy dependence of the scattering at a fixed angle. Figure 13–15 shows the results obtained by Rutherford and Chadwick for the 90° scattering from aluminum. A decrease from inverse-square scattering can be observed to begin at roughly the separation found by Bieler. Attempts were made to fit the observed angular distributions by assuming specific forms for the short-range, non-Coulomb part of the interaction between nucleus and α-particle. These efforts were not successful.

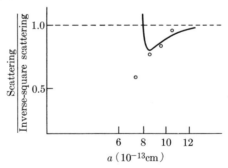

FIG. 3–15. Energy dependence of the 90° scattering of α-particles by aluminum. The abscissa is the distance of closest approach, $a = 2(1 + \sqrt{2})Ze^2/mv^2$, on the assumption of an inverse-square force [see Eqs. (3–31), (3–32)]. It is therefore proportional to $1/E$. The ordinate is the ratio of the observed scattering to that predicted by the Rutherford law. The solid curve gives the theoretical prediction based on a small inverse-fifth-power correction to the Coulomb force.

The experiments we have cited were followed by more accurate ones, which confirmed that an attractive force exists between the constituents of nuclei at separations of a few times 10^{-13} cm. They also verified the validity of Coulomb's law down to at least 10^{-12} cm, a distance very much smaller than any previous data had indicated. At the present day, it still remains an active field of research to investigate whether a breakdown of Coulomb's law takes place at still smaller separations.

We have seen that the nuclear atom is compatible with all the scattering evidence and provides a natural explanation for the radioactive displacement law. Nevertheless, the model is not without its serious difficulties, nearly all connected with electromagnetic properties. Since the electrons outside the nucleus are necessarily in motion, one is faced with the problem of radiative instability, just as in the dynamic version of the Thomson model. Actually, the situation is even worse. A Thomson atom, according to classical electromagnetic theory, would radiate until it reached a static equilibrium configuration. On the other hand, an electron circling a nucleus would spiral inward and fall into the nucleus within a short time; while doing this it would radiate a huge amount of energy. The spectrum which classical theory predicts for a nuclear atom bears little resemblance to any actually observed. Finally, it was not at all clear how the chemical properties of the elements were to be explained on the basis of a nuclear atom. All these problems are discussed in detail in the following volume; none of the difficulties could be resolved without the drastic changes in the classical point of view which came with Bohr's theory.

One final remark should be made concerning alpha-particle scattering and the nuclear model. Rutherford's theory was, of course, based on a "classical" description of the scattering in terms of well-defined orbits, impact parameters, etc. Within fifteen years, however, it had been dramatically demonstrated that such a description is not applicable to atomic phenomena. In general, the quantum-mechanical treatment of scattering from a given field of force leads to results quite different from the classical description of the same problem. Nevertheless, by a remarkable coincidence, the angular distribution in the scattering by an inverse-square force is exactly the same in the two descriptions. In this respect, the success of Rutherford's theory, the discovery of the nucleus, and the formulation of the Bohr atom (which was based on the nuclear model) are all to be considered a stroke of good fortune. Without this coincidence, the progress of modern physics might have been delayed for many years.

REFERENCES

1. F. PERRIN, *Comptes rendus* **121**, (1895).

2. E. T. WHITTAKER, *A History of the Theories of Aether and Electricity.* New York: Harper Torchbooks, 1960, vol. 1, p. 353.

3. P. LENARD, *Ann. der Physik* **51**, 225 (1894); **52**, 23 (1894).

4. J. J. THOMSON, *Phil. Mag.* **44**, 293 (1897).

5. W. KAUFMANN, *Ann. der Physik* **61**, 544 (1897); **62**, 596 (1897).

6. E. WIECHERT, *Königsberg Sitzungsber.* (1897) p. 1; *Ann. der Physik* **69**, 739 (1899).

7. E. GOLDSTEIN, *Berlin Sitzungsber.* **39**, 691 (1886).

8. W. WIEN, *Wien. Ann.* **65**, 440 (1898); *Ann. der Physik* **8**, 224 (1902).

9. J. J. THOMSON, *Phil. Mag.* **13**, 561 (1907).

10. K. T. BAINBRIDGE, an article in *Experimental Nuclear Physics*, Vol. I, E. Segrè, Ed. New York: Wiley, 1953.

11. EVERLING, KÖNIG, MATTAUCH, and WAPSTRA, *Nucl. Phys.* **18**, 529 (1960).

12. O. LODGE, *Electrons.* London: G. Bell and Sons, 5th Ed., 1919.

13. J. J. THOMSON, *Phil. Mag.* **11**, 769 (1906).

14. H. A. WILSON, *Proc. Am. Phil. Soc.* **1**, 366 (1911).

15. J. J. THOMSON, *Phil. Mag.* **7**, 237 (1904).

16. J. J. THOMSON, *Electricity and Matter.* London: Constable and Co., 1904.

17. J. J. THOMSON, *Corpuscular Theory of Matter.* London: Constable and Co., 1907.

18. W. KAUFMANN, *Göttingen Nach.* **2**, 143 (1901).

19. A. H. BUCHERER, *Ann. der Physik* **28**, 513 (1909).

20. M. GOLDHABER and G. SCHARFF-GOLDHABER, *Phys. Rev.* **73**, 1472 (1948).

21. E. RUTHERFORD and T. ROYDS, *Phil. Mag.* **17**, 281 (1909).

22. E. RUTHERFORD and H. ROBINSON, *Phil. Mag.* **28**, 552 (1914).

23. E. RUTHERFORD and H. GEIGER, *Proc. Roy. Soc.* **A81**, 141 (1908).

24. S. GLASSTONE, *Sourcebook on Atomic Energy.* Princeton: Van Nostrand Co., 1950, p. 198.

25. E. RUTHERFORD, H. ROBINSON, and W. F. RAWLINSON, *Phil. Mag.* **28**, 281 (1914).

26. J. CHADWICK, *Verh. d. D. Phys. Ges.* **16**, 383 (1914).

27. E. RUTHERFORD, J. CHADWICK and C. D. ELLIS, *Radiations from Radioactive Substances.* Cambridge: the University Press, 1930.

28. J. J. THOMSON, *Proc. Camb. Phil. Soc.* **15**, 465 (1910).

29. J. A. CROWTHER, *Proc. Roy. Soc.* **A84**, 226 (1910).

30. E. RUTHERFORD, *Phil. Mag.* **21**, 669 (1911).

31. H. GEIGER, *Proc. Roy. Soc.* **A81**, 174 (1908); **A83**, 492 (1910).

32. H. GEIGER and E. MARSDEN, *Proc. Roy. Soc.* **A82**, 495 (1909); **A83**, 492 (1910).

33. H. NAGAOKA, *Phil. Mag.* **7**, 445 (1904).

34. H. GEIGER and E. MARSDEN, *Phil. Mag.* **25**, 604 (1913).

35. J. CHADWICK, *Phil. Mag.* **40**, 734 (1920).

36. C. G. DARWIN, *Phil. Mag.* **27**, 499 (1914).

37. E. RUTHERFORD and J. CHADWICK, *Phil. Mag.* **50**, 889 (1925).

38. E. S. BIELER, *Proc. Roy. Soc.* **A105**, 434 (1924).

PROBLEMS

1. For a four-electron Thomson atom, find the equilibrium positions of the
electrons when they are arranged
    (a) at the corners of a square;
    (b) in an equilateral triangle, with the fourth electron at the center.
Show that configuration (a) has a lower energy.
    Consider the effects of small displacements from equilibrium, both in the
plane of the electrons and perpendicular to this plane. Show that configuration
(b) is stable, while (a) is not.
    Let the electrons rotate about the center of the atom with angular velocity
ω. Find the new equilibrium radii. Show that if the rotation is rapid enough,
configuration (a) becomes stable. Find the value of the minimum frequency
necessary for stability.

2. Spherical projectiles of radius a are incident on a target which consists of
spheres of radius b. Discuss the angular distribution to be expected if the collisions are elastic and single scattering is assumed to be dominant. What is
the effect of assuming various relative masses for the incident particles and the
scatterers?

3. (a) Show by geometry that if a particle of charge Z is scattered by a nucleus
of charge Z_N, the distance of closest approach is given by

$$a = \frac{b}{2}\left(1 + \csc\frac{\theta}{2}\right),$$

where θ is the scattering angle and b the distance of closest approach in a head-
on collision.
    (b) Obtain the same result from the conservation of energy and angular
momentum, using Eqs. (3–30) and (3–31).

4. A point nucleus is surrounded by a thin spherical shell of radius R which
carries a negative charge equal in magnitude to the charge of the nucleus. Show
that if charged particles bombard such a system with an impact parameter p,
the scattering angle is given by

$$\tan\frac{\theta}{2} = \frac{b}{2p}\frac{\sqrt{1 - (p/R)^2}}{1 + b/2R}, \qquad p < R$$

where b is the distance of closest approach for a head-on collision with the bare
nucleus.
    If the incident particles are α's of energy 2 Mev, the nucleus is gold, and R
is of the order of the atomic radius, at what scattering angle does the factor

$$\frac{\sqrt{1 - (p/R)^2}}{1 + b/2R},$$

which represents the screening effect of the shell, become important?

THE LAGRANGE MULTIPLIERS

The problem is to find the maximum of the function of n variables $f(x_1, \ldots, x_n)$, subject to the m conditions

$$g_k(x_1, \ldots, x_n) = 0, \qquad k = 1, \ldots, m. \tag{1A-1}$$

At an extremum, the variation in f induced by variations δx_i must vanish:

$$\delta f = \sum_{i=1}^{n} \frac{\partial f}{\partial x_i} \delta x_i = 0. \tag{1A-2}$$

However, the variations δx_i are not independent. If conditions (1A–1) are to be maintained, we must have

$$\delta g_k = \sum_{i=1}^{n} \frac{\partial g_k}{\partial x_i} \delta x_i = 0, \qquad k = 1, \ldots, m. \tag{1A-3}$$

These m equations enable us to solve for the first m δx_i in terms of the others, so long as the $m \times m$ determinant

$$\left| \frac{\partial g_k}{\partial x_i} \right|, \qquad k, i = 1, \ldots, \mathrm{m},$$

does not vanish. If we add to Eq. (1A–2) the expression

$$\sum_{k=1}^{m} \alpha_k \delta g_k,$$

which is of course zero by virtue of (1A–3), we get

$$\sum_{i=1}^{n} \left\{ \frac{\partial f}{\partial x_i} + \sum_{k=1}^{m} \alpha_k \frac{\partial g_k}{\partial x_i} \right\} \delta x_i = 0. \tag{1A-4}$$

The α_k are, thus far, arbitrary. We now choose them so as to satisfy

$$\frac{\partial f}{\partial x_i} + \sum_{k=1}^{m} \alpha_k \frac{\partial g_k}{\partial x_i} = 0, \qquad k, i = 1, \ldots, m. \tag{1A-5}$$

The condition that this may be done is the nonvanishing of the same determinant $|\partial g_k / \partial x_i|$ which has already been demanded. Equation (1A–5) enables us to rewrite Eq. (1A–4) with the summation restricted to the range $i = m + 1$ to n. But for this range the δx_i are arbitrary, so the vanishing of (1A–4) requires that (1A–5) hold also for the remaining values $i = m + 1, \ldots, n$.

We now define

$$F = f + \sum_{k=1}^{m} \alpha_k g_k \tag{1A-6}$$

and consider F a function of the $n + m$ variables x_i, α_k, with no restrictions. The extremum of F is found from the $n + m$ equations

$$\frac{\partial F}{\partial x_i} = 0, \qquad \frac{\partial F}{\partial \alpha_k} = 0.$$

The latter of these constitutes Eq. (1A–1) and the former, Eq. (1A–5). Hence an extremum of F is also one of f, subject to the prescribed conditions. It is, of course, necessary to verify that the extremum is indeed a maximum.

APPENDIX 2

THE FLOW OF MOLECULES ACROSS AN AREA

We wish to calculate the number of molecules which cross a horizontal area dA in each direction in unit time. Place the area at the origin (Fig. A–1). Consider first those molecules which move with speed between v and $v + dv$; their number density is $n(v)\, dv$. In order to cross the area while moving upward, they must have started from somewhere within the lower hemisphere of radius v. If a molecule starts at the point (r, θ, ϕ) its chance of crossing dA is $1/4\pi$ times the solid angle subtended by dA at that point, or

$$\frac{1}{4\pi} \frac{dA}{r^2} \cos\theta. \tag{2A–1}$$

The number of molecules with speed v which cross in unit time is therefore

$$\int_0^v r^2\, dr \int_0^{\pi/2} \sin\theta\, d\theta \int_0^{2\pi} d\phi\, n(v)\, dv \left(\frac{1}{4\pi} \frac{dA}{r^2} \cos\theta\right) = \frac{1}{4} v n(v)\, dv\, dA. \tag{2A–2}$$

To find the total number of molecules crossing, we must integrate this expression over v. But the integral $\int_0^\infty v n(v)\, dv$ by definition, is n times the average speed $\bar{v}$. Therefore the total number of molecules which cross per unit area is $\frac{1}{4} n \bar{v}$. The result is clearly independent of the form of the velocity distribution.

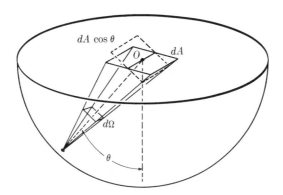

FIGURE A–1

APPENDIX 3

SCATTERING IN AN INVERSE-SQUARE FIELD

We present here a simple derivation of the deflection of a charged particle by a Coulomb field. Let $Z'e$ and m be the charge and mass of the incident particle. Assume at first that the scatterer of charge Ze is heavy enough to be considered fixed in place, at point O in Fig. A–2. The path of the moving particle is shown by the solid curve. The dashed line CD indicates the path which the incident particle would follow if no deflecting field were present; the impact parameter p is the perpendicular from O to CD. Line AB is drawn through O and the point of closest approach of the moving particle. The path must be symmetric about AB. If ϕ is the angle between CD and AB, then the scattering angle θ is given by

$$\theta = \pi - 2\phi. \tag{3A–1}$$

We seek the relation between ϕ, p, and the initial velocity v. Consider the component of momentum Π_l along the direction AB. Its initial value is $mv \cos \phi$; the component of force in this direction AB is

$$F_l = \frac{ZZ'e^2}{r^2} \cos y, \tag{3A–2}$$

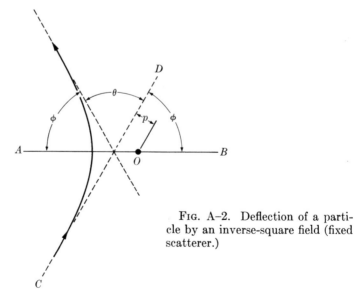

Fig. A–2. Deflection of a particle by an inverse-square field (fixed scatterer.)

110

where y is the angle which the instantaneous radius vector $\mathbf{r}$ makes with AB. (Notice that at the initial point on the trajectory, y has the value $\phi + \pi$, that is, $\cos y$ is negative.) Consequently the momentum Π_l is given by

$$\Pi_l = mv \cos \phi + ZZ'e^2 \int_{\phi+\pi}^{y} \frac{\cos y}{r^2} \frac{dt}{dy} \, dy. \tag{3A-3}$$

The angular momentum about O is $mr^2 \, dy/dt$ and is a constant of the motion since the force is central. When the moving particle is at infinity, its angular momentum is $-mvp$. Consequently,

$$mr^2 \frac{dy}{dt} = - mvp. \tag{3A-4}$$

Introducing this equality into the integral (3A–3), we obtain

$$\Pi_l = mv \cos \phi - \frac{ZZ'e^2}{vp} \int_{\phi+\pi}^{y} \cos y \, dy$$

$$= mv \cos \phi - \frac{ZZ'e^2}{vp} (\sin y + \sin \phi). \tag{3A-5}$$

When $y = \pi$, at the point of closest approach, Π_l passes through zero. Hence Eq. (3A–5) implies that

$$p = \frac{ZZ'e^2}{mv^2} \tan \phi. \tag{3A-6}$$

Using Eq. (3A–1) to express this result in terms of θ, we obtain Eq. (3–30) of the main text.

When the target particle is not treated as infinitely massive, the motion is most conveniently viewed in the coordinate system in which the center of mass is at rest at the origin. In this frame the coordinates of the two particles are related by

$$\mathbf{r}_2^* = - \left(\frac{m_1}{m_2}\right) r_1^*, \tag{3A-7}$$

with a similar relation for the velocities. [Asterisks are used to denote center-of-mass (CM) quantities.] If in the laboratory, particle 1 has velocity $\mathbf{v}$ and particle 2 is at rest, the CM-system moves relative to the laboratory with velocity

$$\mathbf{v}_{\text{CM}} - \mathbf{v} \frac{m_1}{m_1 + m_2} \tag{3A-8}$$

The initial and final configurations in the laboratory and in the CM-

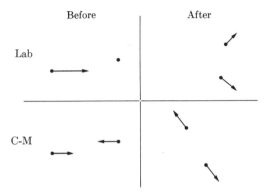

FIG. A–3. Collision between moving and stationary particle as seen in laboratory and in center-of-mass systems.

systems are compared in Fig. A–3. The force on particle 1 in the CM-system points away from the origin and has the magnitude

$$F_1^* = \frac{ZZ'e^2}{r_1^{*2}[(m_1 + m_2)/m_2]^2}. \tag{3A-9}$$

The motion of the particle is therefore the same as though it were acted on by a charge $Z_{\text{eff}} = Z[m_2/(m_1 + m_2)]^2$ at the origin, and the deflection is given by the derivation presented above:

$$\tan \frac{\theta^*}{2} = \frac{Z'Z_{\text{eff}}e^2}{m_1 v^{*2} p^*}. \tag{3A-10}$$

Here v^* and p^* are the initial velocity and impact parameter with respect to the origin in the CM-system, and are given by

$$v^* = v \frac{m_2}{m_1 + m_2} \tag{3A-11}$$

and

$$p^* = p \frac{m_2}{m_1 + m_2}. \tag{3A-12}$$

Hence (3A–10) has the form

$$\tan \frac{\theta^*}{2} = \frac{ZZ'e^2}{v^2 p[m_1 m_2/(m_1 + m_2)]}. \tag{3A-13}$$

To relate θ^* with θ, the laboratory scattering angle, we use the fact that the components of velocity transverse to the incident direction are the same in the two systems, whereas the longitudinal components differ by

v_{CM}, Eq. (3A–8). From this it follows directly that

$$\tan \theta = \frac{\sin \theta^*}{\cos \theta* + m_1/m_2} \, . \tag{3A–14}$$

When the masses are equal, the relations are quite simple. Equation (3A–14) becomes merely $\theta = \frac{1}{2}\theta^*$, and (3A–13) becomes

$$\tan \theta = \frac{2ZZ'e^2}{mv^2p} \, , \tag{3A–15}$$

which is Eq. (3–20) of the text.

When the incident particle is extremely fast, so that the scattering angle is small, the scattering angle may be obtained from the following simple argument. The collision takes place so quickly that the target particle has no time to recoil. That is, the target remains approximately fixed during the time of the collision even though its mass may be small (impulse approximation). Furthermore, the component of momentum of the incident particle in its original direction remains essentially unchanged. The transverse momentum acquired can be calculated, under these assumptions, by integrating the transverse component of force. Let the incident velocity be in the y-direction, and let α be the angle between the x-axis and the instantaneous radius vector. The transverse force is then

$$F_x = \frac{ZZ'e^2}{p^2 + y^2} \cos \alpha = \frac{ZZ'e^2 p}{(p^2 + v^2 t^2)^{3/2}} \, . \tag{3A–16}$$

Consequently, the x-momentum acquired is

$$p_x = 2 \int_0^\infty F_x \, dt$$

$$= \frac{2ZZ'e^2}{pv} \, . \tag{3A–17}$$

This gives

$$\theta \approx \frac{p_x}{p_y} = \frac{2ZZ'e^2}{mv^2p} \, . \tag{3A–18}$$

This is the form obtained from (3A–13) and (3A–14) in the limit of high velocity and small scattering angle, no matter what the masses of the particles may be.

INDEX

Absorption, of beta and cathode rays, 52, 67, 83, 88
Absorption spectrum, 72
Abundance of isotopes, 64
Aether, 52
All-electron atom, 66–67
Alpha particles, 8, 9, 74–83, 89–97, 100–102
   charge of, 9, 76–78
   identification of, 74–78
   range-energy relation for, 81–82
   scattering of, 87, 89–97, 100–102
   specific charge of, 76
   velocity of, 80–81
Alpha rays; *see* alpha particles
Anderson, 66
Andrade, 78
Angular distribution
   in α-particle scattering, 93–94, 96–97, 100–102
   in β-ray scattering, 84–88
   in rigid-sphere scattering, 104
Artificial molecules (Perrin), 6–8, 9, 17
Aston, 63
Atmospheres, law of, 6, 7, 20, 26, 27
   and Maxwell-Boltzmann distribution, 27–29
Atomic dimensions, 2, 6, 46
   hypothesis, 1–7, 9, 12
   masses, 2, 9, 63–65
      table of, 64
   mass unit, 8, 63
   models, *see* Lenard, Nagaoka, Rutherford, Thomson
   number and nuclear charge, 98–99
Avogadro's hypothesis, 1, 2
   number, 2, 3, 4, 6, 8–10, 21, 44

Bainbridge, 61, 62
Barkla, 88, 89
Barometer formula; *see* Atmospheres, law of
Becker, 23
Becquerel, 51, 58, 74, 75

Beta rays (particles), 5, 58, 74–75, 79, 82–89, 99
   absorption of, 67, 83
   continuous velocity spectrum, 75, 82–83
   identification of, 74–75
   line spectrum, 82–83
   scattering of, 83–89, 99
   specific charge of, 58, 75
   velocity of, 82–83
Bieler, 101–102
Binding energy, 65, 89, 99
Binomial coefficient, 21
Blackbody radiation, 8, 32
Bohr atom, 103
Boltwood, 9
Boltzmann, 27, 28, 41
Boltzmann distribution; *see* Maxwell-Boltzmann distribution
Boltzmann factor, 31, 32
Boltzmann's constant, 8, 14
Brownian motion, 7, 16–17, 21, 48
Bucherer, 75

Canal rays, 50, 59–61
Carbon 12, mass scale, 2, 63–65
Cathode rays, 5, 50, 51–58, 67, 75
   absorption of, 52, 57, 67
   identity with beta rays, 58, 74–75
   specific charge of, 52–55
   velocity of, 52, 54
Center-of-mass system, 111–113
Chadwick, 75, 82–83, 98–99, 101, 102
Charge, atomic nature of, 3, 9–10
   of α-particle, 9, 76–78
   of electron, 4–6, 23, 58–59
   of nucleus, 95–99
   of positive ions, 59
Charge-to-mass ratio, *see* specific charge
Chemical mass scale, 63
Clausius, 14
Closest approach, distance of, 91, 105
Cloud chamber, 74, 78, 81